EXPLORATIONS IN BIOLOGY
LAB MANUAL FOR BISC 131 AND 133
BIOLOGICAL PRINCIPLES AND BIOLOGICAL DIVERSITY

Sixth Edition

Wes Colgan III
Linda Ramsey
James D. White
Jim Spaulding

Louisiana Tech University
Ruston, Louisiana

Learning Solutions

New York   Boston   San Francisco
London   Toronto   Sydney   Tokyo   Singapore   Madrid
Mexico City   Munich   Paris   Cape Town   Hong Kong   Montreal

Pearson Learning Solutions, 501 Boylston Street, Suite 900, Boston, MA 02116
A Pearson Education Company
www.pearsoned.com

Printed in the United States of America

15 16 17 V0CR 15 14

000200010270585269

MHB/CA

ISBN 10: 0-558-74221-1
ISBN 13: 978-0-558-74221-8

CONTENTS

Preface   v

Introduction: How to Keep a Lab Notebook   1

1 The Student Lab Report   3

2 Introduction to Investigations   13

3 The Microscope as a Tool for Investigation   19

4 Environmental Pollution Control   29

5 Environmental Pollution   33

6 Diffusion and Osmosis   39

7 Enzyme Activity   45

8 Photosynthesis   53

9 Cellular Respiration   59

10   Independent Study   63

11   Mendelian and Human Genetics   67

12   Introduction to Classification of Organisms   81

13   Class Research Project: Habitat Description   87

14   Domains Bacteria and Archea   97

15   Domain Eukarya, Kingdoms Protista and Fungi   105

16   Domain Eukarya, Kingdom Plantae   117

17   Domain Eukarya, Kingdom Plantae Seed Bearing Plants: Spermatophyta   127

18   Kingdom Animalia   139

19   The Vertebrate Chordates   165

PREFACE

In this lab manual you will find a number of lab experiments and exercises that are designed to familiarize you with the tools, technology, and methods employed by scientists. These labs come from our collective experiences as instructors in undergraduate biology laboratories and science education.

As students in this course you'll be helping us assess some of the success of these exercises throughout the term. These exercises are designed for you to hone your skills and act as scientists rather than memorizing a vast amount of cool sounding terminology to regurgitate back to us (you will get plenty of this aspect in the lecture class). Please keep in mind that the tools and technologies you will be using are the same ones used by professional scientists today.

As future scientists, professionals, and voting citizens we hope these experiences will give you a deeper understanding that science is a process. The next time you hear someone say, "We have reached the limits of science" you'll understand why that that will never happen. Science is a **process** and a **way of knowing,** and is therefore limitless. Nothing is sacred in science. Scientific knowledge is based on our best explanation of the physical processes at work in the system we are studying. If new information comes to light that contradicts the current state knowledge, we will **CHANGE** our explanation. Matters of faith (things we believe without the bias of fact) are therefore beyond the realm of science.

There are four rules we must be aware of as biological researchers:

Rule No. 1: *Whatever you study don't do it with your own money.* This is why we have granting agencies such as the National Science Foundation.

Rule No. 2: *Whatever you are working on, it will never, ever, ever, ever work right the first time.* This is a function of the inherent variability in any biological system as well as some of the random perversity of the Universe.

Rule No. 3: This is the most important rule for working in the laboratory. *Never, regardless of what you're working with, get any of that stuff on you.* This is good lab practice. It will be employed throughout the term even though we will be working primarily with harmless chemicals and common everyday items. This is an excellent habit to learn early because one day you may work in a hot lab where this rule could mean the difference between a successful career or a very, very short one.

Rule No. 4: *Studying biology has to be fun.* To be a successful researcher you have to love going to the lab every day. If you do not find biological research to be a fun and joyous experience, consider changing your major. You will make much more money by getting a degree from one of those other units on campus. The likelihood of becoming rich and famous by devoting your life to biology is SMALL. If the biological sciences are your calling, however, you will find it to be one of the most satisfying, joyful, and meaningful ways you can spend your time on planet Earth.

ACKNOWLEDGMENTS

This lab manual would not have been possible without the help of a vast number of friends and colleagues with whom we've been involved with over the years.

First we would like to thank J. Page Lindsay and John M. Condie from Fort Lewis College in Durango, Colorado whose lab manual "Experiments in Cell Biology" was the inspiration for this manual and from which we have borrowed extensively.

We must thank our students without whom we wouldn't be here. Seeing the biological world through their eyes, watching them make new discoveries, and view the living world in a new way is the reason we became biology educators.

We would like to thank Dr. John Measel, Former Director for the School Biological Sciences, Louisiana Tech University for giving us the flexibility to develop this course and this lab manual.

We would also like to thank the authors of a great number of laboratory manuals that we looked at during the production of this manual for inspiring us to develop our own.

Chapters 13–19 were inspired in large part by The Lab Manual for Organismal Biology: an Evolutionary Approach by Michael G. Simpson Erik W. A. Gergus and Scott C. McMillan. Burgess Publishing Inc. 1998.

Finally we would like to thank our graduate students, Narcissa Bagwell, Teresa Buckley, Julie Dubois, Jason Hill, Shelly Rabalais, and Katie Sandel, who fearlessly taught these labs, graded the papers, heard all of the complaints, and made many useful comments on the second edition of this manual.

INTRODUCTION

HOW TO KEEP A LAB NOTEBOOK

Record keeping is one of the most important functions we have to perform to be good scientists. How many times have you gotten to the store only to realize you forgot your list and had to say to yourself "I can't remember what I needed to get to bake that cake." The next day you began mixing the batter only to find you forgot to buy the eggs! When baking a cake you can always stop and run back to the store to pick up the eggs and be back, without anyone ever noticing. With science, however, once your manuscript is published and becomes part of our knowledge base it is forever part of the history of science. A scientist must keep track of all of the components of his or her given experiments. To do this we must keep careful records in the lab.

For this course you will need a **dedicated lab notebook.** Your instructor will show you the first day of classes what kind of book you'll need to purchase. Your lecture notes and other little nuggets of goodness will need to be kept elsewhere. Periodically this notebook will be collected and graded; we cannot afford to have you say "But I need my notes for the lecture test tomorrow." Having a dedicated lab notebook, this will not be a problem.

Begin each new class session on a new page. This will help eliminate confusion for your lab instructor. (This helps your grade!) In laboratory #1, you'll conduct an observational experiment with termites and one using a microscope to investigate a freshwater pond community. Begin on page one, and title this exercise "Introduction to Investigation" (or your equally interesting and appropriate title) and the date. The next portion will contain your hypothesis. Remember, the hypothesis is your presumed answer to the question you are asking. Your hypothesis is just an educated guess so use your best powers of observation. Your hypothesis may sometimes be stated as a question but usually it is a declarative statement, such as:

"Single cell green algae are the dominant life form in pond scum."

Next you'll want to set up your materials and methods section. The materials are the items you will use to conduct your experiment (your shopping list). If you are using the procedure outlined in this lab manual, just write in your lab notebook "see page such and such in the lab manual." This way you can go back and find it if you need to dredge up the information. **If your procedures vary from the lab manual in any way, be sure to note it here. This is different than the methods section in your lab reports (see the sample write-up this volume).** The next section is your actual data. Sometimes this will be a list, sometimes a table; sometimes this will be illustrations of the creatures you observed through the microscope. Keeping accurate records of numerical data is essential. Any corrections such as missed decimal places or other clerical or typographical errors should be noted and explained in your lab notebook. Do not just cross out the bad data and write in the good data as this may be interpreted as "cooking" your results.

There have been many cases of scientists "cooking" their data. Does anyone remember scientists by the names of M. Fleischmann and S. Pons? These scientists claimed to have discovered cold fusion (a cheap source of potentially unlimited energy). When scientists at other institutions tried to duplicate their data, they found that Fleischmann and Pons had not only *not* discovered a cheap source of energy, but also had failed to report data that was contradictory to the claims they were making. Omitting data that refutes your hypothesis is called fraud. Scientists will always report data that refutes as well as the data that supports their hypothesis. Zeros are data, too.

Most of your lab notebook entries will end here. Occasionally you may want to jot down some notes or other observations, or potentially a brief analysis of your "raw" data.

Keeping careful notes in a neat and orderly fashion will make the final step of the scientific process (the writing and dispensing of the data you collected) much easier and less time consuming. Trust us, we have been doing this for a while. Rushing to get out of the lab early will cost you later down the road; it always does.

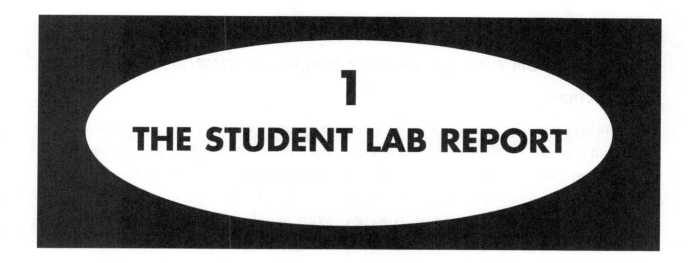

1
THE STUDENT LAB REPORT

This example lab report is designed to serve as a template on which you can "hang" your data. DO NOT assume that that you have to follow this example exactly, but you will find the five basic sections in every scientific paper.

Introduction: This section includes the problem, idea, and your hypothesis. That is why this is interesting stuff and worth writing down and how it relates to our knowledge of our world.

Methods: This is *what you did,* NOT A BETTY CROCKER "DO THIS" LIST! This is where you tell your peers *what you did* with enough detail so that another scientist could duplicate your conditions and treatments.

Results: This is where you present the important data you collected and any interesting trends or anomalies. DO NOT PRESENT RAW DATA! Present only the important findings. For example, you may have run 4 replicates of each of your treatments, and averaged them to gain a better estimate of your treatment effects. We don't need to know the actual numbers for all of your replicates. Showing this raw data wastes paper and time when the average of the replicates is the important number that shows the treatment effect.

Discussion: This is where you get to go out on the limb and talk about what your data means, why it is cool, and why you deserve a Nobel prize. The other critical element of the discussion is describing the shortcomings of your data. No study is perfect, so don't expect yours to be. You may want to answer the following questions: What would you do differently? How could the study be improved? What deserves further study? What was a dead end? Be sure to relate your work to that of others in the field.

References Cited: This is not a bibliography (a list of every related written material you could find). This will include only the actual web pages/articles/books that you cite in your report. Examples of each citation format are shown in the sample lab report. Be very careful about web pages. Many are good and frequently maintained by actual scientists, some are Billy-Bob's class notes from 1976 and aren't worth anything. When in doubt, ask your instructor. Encyclopedias are NOT appropriate sources for college level research.

A TYPICAL STUDENT-DESIGNED PROJECT

EFFECT OF PH ON THE GROWTH OF THE FUNGUS *NEUROSOPERA CRASSA*

INTRODUCTION

Fungi are critically important members of every ecosystem on earth. They are decomposers, parasites, and mutualists with virtually every other living creature. It has been estimated that fungi occupy about 25% of the biomass on planet earth (Alexopolous *et al.,* 1996). Acid rain causes may effects in our ecosystems by lowering the pH of soils, lakes and streams. Acid rain is a byproduct of human use of fossil fuels (US EPA, 2000). For our study we looked at the common bread mold and its growth responses to media of varying pH. *Neurospora* has been used for a number of studies including the Nobel prize-winning genetics work of Beadle and Tatum (1965). Various other studies have shown some fungi to be sensitive to the effect of acid rain (Agerer, 1988). We believe *Neurospora* will show some sensitivity to its environment and will serve as a model organism in our study simulating acid rain.

METHODS

Our culture of *Neurospora* was obtained from the Carolina Biological Supply Company and stock cultures were maintained according to label instructions. Potato dextrose agar was prepared according to label directions. This was then sterilized for 15 minutes at 121°C at 15lb/psi. Three portions were then poured into sterile beakers and the pH of each was adjusted using citrate buffers. The control media was buffered to pH 7.0, the next was adjusted to pH 6.0, and the third adjusted to pH 5.0 as measured with a Fisher portable pH meter. The liquid agar was then poured into sterile petri dishes and allowed to cool. Four plates for each treatment were inoculated with a small fragment of the growing mycelium from the stock culture. Growth was recorded at three-day intervals by measuring the diameter of the colony for a total of nine days.

RESULT

After nine days, all 12 plates showed growth. Colonies grown on media at pH 7.0 showed the greatest diameter increase while colonies grown at pH 5.0 showed the least. Diameter growth of the four replicates for each treatment were averaged and plotted in Figure 1. Contamination was evident in a single plate at pH 5; a small black mold was seen growing in this plate. It was therefore excluded from the analysis.

DISCUSSION

It would appear that *Neurospora* grows better on media with a pH closer to neutral than at lower pH. This data support the observations by Agerer (1988) that acidifying environment is bad for

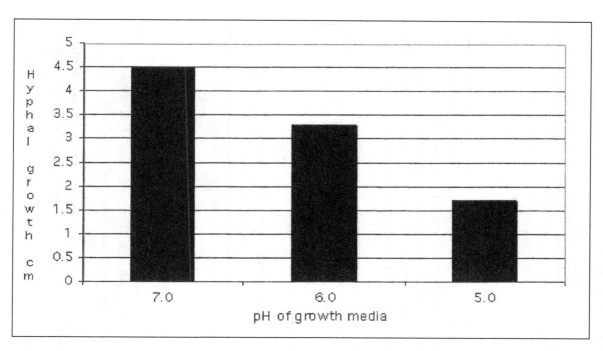

FIGURE 1.   Growth of Neurospora on media of different pH, Average of 4 replicates (pH 5 only 3 replicates were used).

some fungi. It should be noted, however, that other researchers have found some fungi that prefer to grow at lower pH (Alexopolous et al., 1996). The single plate that was contaminated showed a vigorous growth of a black colored mold. The contamination could have come from the air as the plates were being poured. The colony of *Neurospora* in this plate appeared to grow at the same rate as the others in its treatment group, however on the side of the plate closest to the competing mold it appeared that the approaching hyphae had suppressed each others growth. This is an interesting interaction between these two species that may occur in nature. However, as it is outside the scope of this study, we excluded this individual from our analysis. Future studies should explore pH above 7.0 and potentially units between 6.0 and 7.0 to find the optimal growth for this species of *Neurospora*.

REFERENCES CITED

Alexopoulos, C.J., C.W. Mims, & M. Blackwell. 1996. *Introductory Mycology.* John Wiley and Sons. 526 pp.

Agerer, R. 1988. Impact of artificial acid rain and liming on fruitbody production of ectomycorrhizal fungi., In, Mejstrik, V. (ed.). *Proc. 2nd European Symposium on Mycorrhizae.* August, 1988. Prague, Czechoslovakia. p. 3–4.

Beadle, G.W. and E.L. Tatum. 1942. Genetic control of biochemical reactions in Neurospora. *Proceedings of the National Academy of Science,* 27:499–507.

US EPA Acid Rain Home Page. [web page], 24 April 1995; www.epa.gov/acidrain/ardhome.html [Accessed May 22, 2000].

COMPONENTS OF A LABORATORY REPORT

SECTION	QUESTION	EXAMPLE
TITLE The title should relate the independent and dependent variable that were investigated.	What are you testing?	The Effect of Aspirin On the Growth Of Tomato Plants The Effect of Water Temperature on the Dissolving Time of Effervescent Tablets Effect of pH on the Growth of *Neurospora crassa*.
INTRODUCTION This section establishes the research problem by giving the rational, purpose, and hypothesis for the study.	1) Why did you conduct the experiment? (rationale) The answer to this question explains why studying this topic is important. Relevant research from other scientists should be cited.	Fungi are critically important members of every ecosystem on earth. They are decomposers, parasites, and mutualists with many other creatures. It has been estimated that fungi occupy about 25% of the biomass on planet earth (Alexopolous et al 1996). In Louisiana, for example, fungi are critical to the rapid growth of pine trees. Various studies have shown that some fungi are sensitive to acid rain (Agerer, 1988). Acid rain causes many effects in our ecosystems by lowering the pH of soils, lakes, and streams. Changes in pH of the soils might affect the growth and reproduction of fungi that inhabit the soils. Acid reain is a by-product of human use of fossil fuels (US EPA, 2000). As the use of fossil fuels to power our cars, heat our homes, and run our factories increases, the effect on the environment may become more critical. *Neurospora*, the common bread mold, is a fungus that has been used for a number of studies including the Nobel prize-winning genetics work of Beadle and Tatum (1965).
	2) What did you hope to learn? (purpose)	For our study, we looked at the common bread mold and its growth responses to media of different pH values. Or The purpose of the study was to determine the effect on the growth of Neurospora on growth media of different pH values.
	3) What did you think would happen? (hypothesis)	Our hypothesis is that *Neurospora* will grow over a wide range of pH values but will show the largest amount of growth over a narrow range of pH (6.5-7.5). Or The researchers hypothesized that *Neurospora* will grow over a wide range of pH values, but will show the largest amount of growth on media of a very narrow range of pH (6.5 7.5).

COMPONENTS OF A LABORATORY REPORT

SECTION	QUESTION	EXAMPLE
MATERIALS AND METHODS A concise report that describes what you did so that another scientist could replicate the experiment.	1) What did you do?	Potato dextrose agar plates (pH range of 5.0 7.0) were inoculated with a standard *Neurospora* culture.
	2) What equipment, organisms, or compounds did you use?	Our culture of *Neurospora* was obtained from the Carolina Biological Supply Company and stock cultures were maintained according to label instructions. Potato dextrose agar was prepared according to label directions with clean deionized water.
	3) How did you do it?	The potato dextrose agar was then sterilized for 15 minutes at 121 degrees Celsius. Three portions were then poured into sterile beakers and the pH of each was adjusted using citrate buffers. The control media was buffered to pH 7.0, the next was adjusted to pH 6.0, and the third adjusted to pH 5.0 as measured with a Fisher portable pH meter. The liquid agar was then poured into steril petri dishes and allowed to cool. Four plates for each treatment were inoculated with a small fragment of the growing mycelium form the stock culture. Growth was recorded at three day intervals for nine days.
RESULTS Include appropriately labeled data chart and graph. Summarize your data.	1) What kind of graph should you use? 2) How will you label the axes of the graph? 3) What is the title of the graph?	
DISCUSSION	1) Do not repeat data!	

COMPONENTS OF A LABORATORY REPORT

SECTION	QUESTION	EXAMPLE
DISCUSSION (continued)	2) What were the major findings? What pattern did you see?	There was no difference in height of tomato plants that were grown in the presence of the different fertilizers.
		Or
		As the amount of oil in the water increased, the growth of the duckweed decreased. All duckweed died in samples that contained more than 10 ppb oil.
		Or
		After nine days, all 12 plates showed growth. Colonies grown on media at pH 7.0 showed the greatest diameter increase while colonies grown at pH 5.0 showed the least.
		Or
		As the pH increased from pH 5.0 to pH 7.0, the diameter of the colonies also increased.
		Or
		It would appear that Neurospora grows better at a pH closer to neutral than at lower pH.
	3) Was the research hypothesis supported by the data?	The data do not support the original hypothesis that the higher the concentration of nitrogen in the fertilizer, the greater the height of the tomato plants.
		Or
		The data support the hypothesis that the higher the concentration of oil, the slower the duckweed would grow. An unexpected result was the death of all duckweed at such a low concentration (10 ppb).
		Or
		The data agree with the hypothesis that the best growth would be obtained at pH values between 6.5 and 7.5. Data collected are not sufficient to extrapolate to pH values above 7.0.

COMPONENTS OF A LABORATORY REPORT

SECTION	QUESTION	EXAMPLE
DISCUSSION (continued)	5. What possible explanations can you offer for your findings?	It is possible that the amount of regular fertilizer added to the soil lowered the pH to a level that damaged the plants. The slow release fertilizer, although containing the same total amount of phosphorous and nitrogen, releases these compounds a little at a time. The pH is not as severely affected.
		Or
		It appears that the oil is much more toxic to the duckweed than the chemicals found in the paper mill effluent. Perhaps this is because the oil coats the duckweed and prevents the uptake of carbon dioxide thus disrupting photosynthesis.
		Or
		It is possible that the fungi we tested are adapted for growth at a higher pH since they were isolated from very basic soil.
	6. What recommendations do you have for further study and for improving the experiment?	Comparison of the pH of the soil surrounding the plants fertilized with the different fertilizer types would help determine if a decrease in pH was responsible for the decreased growth of the plants.
		Or
		Increasing the pH range over which growth of fungi were compared would increase our confidence in the trend.
		Or
		Increasing the number of replicates would account for any individual variation in organisms that might have been responsible for the differences we observed.

RUBRIC FOR SCORING LABORATORY REPORTS

Criteria	Meets Expectations	Needs Some Improvement	Needs Major Revision
Organization	Title gives clear description of the focus of the article by relating the independent and dependent variables that were investigated; all five sections are present, in the correct order, and information included is appropriate for the section; sections are clearly labeled; references are correct and cited appropriately in a citations section.	Title vague. Information presented in wrong section or incorrectly in more than one section. References cited in text do not appear in citation section or vice versa.	Title misleading. One or more sections missing. Sections not labeled or include inappropriate information. No references or several references incorrectly cited in text and in the citation section.
Grammar/ Spelling	No grammatical or spelling errors.	No more than 3 grammatical and/or spelling errors.	More than 3 grammatical and/or spelling errors.
Writing Style	Writing is clear and concise with no long, rambling sentences or sentence fragments. Unfamiliar ("big") words are avoided, convoluted phrases are avoided, and sentences are short and direct. Active voice used when possible.	Contains some jargon, and a limited number of run-on sentences or sentence fragments. Occasionally shifts inappropriately from active to passive voice or uses wrong verb tense.	Writing style is inappropriate. Too much jargon is used. Convoluted phrases, run-on sentences, and extremely long sentences are numerous. Passive voice is used inappropriately.
Professional Appearance	Paper is neat. Appropriate line spacing and margins are used. Font chosen is appropriate size (12 point) and formality. Graphs and charts have been prepared on computer and are visually attractive. Photographs (if included) are neatly mounted.	Paper lacks polish. Appearance could be improved by use of white space and color on graphs and charts.	Paper is sloppy. Margins too narrow or too large. Font size too small or too large. Graphs, charts, and/or photographs sloppy, visually unattractive, or mounted incorrectly.
Introduction/ Background Information	States problem and explains why the problem is worth studying. Includes literature citations that review previous work in the area, document the problem, and support the importance of the work. Explains the purpose of the research and presents a correctly stated hypothesis.	Problem statement is unclear. Some relevant major work is not cited. Purpose of work is unclear. Hypothesis is not stated clearly.	Fails to state problem and why problem is worth studying. Fails to cite previous work. Does not explain purpose of work. Does not include a testable hypothesis.
Methods	Clearly describes the design of the experiment. Experimental organism is referred to at least once	Experimental design is unclear; design is not presented in a logical sequence.	Experimental design is poor; does not include multiple treatment levels and/or

	by its scientific name; the scientific name is cited properly. Identifies and provides the source for materials/organisms used. Experiment is well designed; includes a testable hypothesis, adequate replications, adequate control of variables, a control group when appropriate, uses appropriate instrumentation and/or techniques, and an appropriate method for measuring/determining results. Identifies the parameter that was varied (independent variable) and the levels at which it was tested. Describes what was measured (dependent variable) and how measurements were made. Reports the number of treatment levels and how many replicates were run at each level. Discusses any critical safety considerations.	Important steps or considerations not fully explained or out of order. Increasing or varying treatment levels could improve design. Design could be improved by increasing number of replicates. Hypothesis and experimental design are not tightly correlated.	replications; does not control variables. Important steps or considerations are left out; experiment is not repeatable with information given. No information is given for source of organisms and instruments. Methods section cannot stand-alone.
Results	Data is presented in data tables and/or graphs that are appropriately set up, titled, and labeled. Raw data have been compiled and only compiled data are presented. Important data trends are summarized and reported; anomalies are reported.	Legends or titles of data tables and/or graphs are misleading. Raw data is presented without summarizing.	Tables and/or graphs missing or not appropriately set up. Table/graph legend is not stand-alone. Anomalies are not reported.
Discussion	Summarizes major findings (does not simply repeat data). Clearly indicates to what level the data supported or did not support the hypothesis. Describes how results compare with those of other researchers; cites appropriate references. Offers explanations for results; supports explanations with references to specific data. Discusses what data means, its importance in the field, and (if appropriate) its societal relevance. Describes shortcomings of current experiment, suggests ways to improve experiment, and outlines future experiments to be performed.	Discussion addresses most major findings but also repeats data. Describes how results compare with other researchers but does not include conflicting results. Offers explanations for results but does not support them with data. Discussion of relevance of work is weak; misses major connections with other significant ideas and issues. Discussion of shortcomings of experiment is weak; author fails to acknowledge significant weaknesses. Future experiments that are outlined will not provide significant data.	Discussion fails to address important findings; does not relate findings to original hypothesis. Fails to compare work to others in the field or does not cite appropriate references. Section simply restates results without drawing conclusions that are supported by data. Fails to describe major shortcomings of experiment or outline future experiments to be performed.
Literature Cited	Cites all references used in an appropriate format.	Wrong format is used for citing references.	No references cited or references cited that are not included in text or references used in text but not cited in this section.

2
INTRODUCTION TO INVESTIGATIONS

OBJECTIVES

Introduce students to the basic tools of scientific discovery.

Allow students to test their hypothesis using a model system.

BACKGROUND INFORMATION

Termites are small to medium-sized insects that live in social groups and have a highly developed caste system. Termites can be winged or wingless. Termites with wings are usually dark colored and are the reproductive members of the colony (kings and queens). Each colony usually has a single queen that is larger than the winged kings. Reproductive, winged termites have compound eyes. A single, mated pair establishes a new colony. Termites with wings have 4 wings that are all the same size and shape and are held flat over the body when the insect is at rest. Wingless non-reproductive termites (workers and soldiers) are generally very light colored and soft bodied. Termite workers and soldiers consist of individuals of both sexes, with all nymphs acting as workers. Workers consist of nymphs and sterile adults; they usually lack compound eyes, and have relatively small mandibles. The soldiers are sterile adults that have greatly enlarged heads and mandibles and are generally darker in color than the workers. Soldiers serve to defend the colony and may have mandibles that are so large they are unable to feed themselves and must be fed by the workers. Termites undergo a 3-stage incomplete metamorphosis (egg, nymph, adult). They feed on cast off skins and feces of other individuals, dead individuals, and plant material such as wood or wood products. Termites digest wood and wood products with the help of a myriad of flagellated protozoa that live in the termite's gut. If the protozoa are removed, the termite will continue to eat but will eventually starve to death because it's food is not digested. Termites often use their mouth parts to groom each other. Termites communicate as do other social insects via volatile chemical compounds called pheromones. These chemicals often serve as alarm triggers, sexual attractants, or trail delineators. Termites are important economic pests that attack structures made of wood. They are also valuable members of the ecosystem and serve as detritivores that aid in the decomposition of rotting logs and tree stumps.

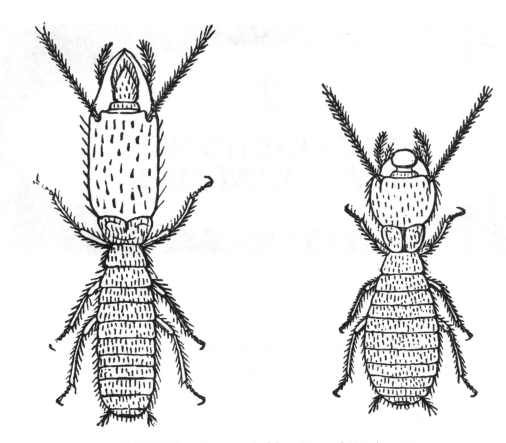

FIGURE 1.   Termite Soldier (L) and Worker (R)

REFERENCES

Borror, Donald J,. and Dwight M. Delong. 1954. *An Introduction to the Study of Insects.* Holt Rhinehart and Winston, New York.

Borror, Donald J. and Richard E. White. 1970. *Insects.* Peterson Field Guide. Houghton Mifflin & Co, Boston.

Imes, Rick. 1992. *The Practical Entomologist.* Simon and Schuster, New York.

MATERIALS FOR ONE GROUP

2 sheets white typing paper
2 sheets dark colored construction paper
Scotch tape
4 magnifiers (3X–6X)
1 paintbrush
2 Bic ballpoint pens - 1 blue ink and 1 black ink
2 Papermate ballpoint pens - 1 blue ink and 1 black ink
Assorted pens of other colors
Ruler
Termites (see your instructor)

PROCEDURE

Use a single sheet of white paper (and some tape if available) to construct a container that will hold several small organisms. The container does not need a lid and should be designed with a large flat surface area and low sides. On the floor of the container draw two circles each about 5cm in diameter and about 2.5cm apart. The circles should be drawn with the Bic pens; one with the blue pen and one with the black pen. In your lab notebook, divide a page into two columns; label one column Observations and one column Inferences/Questions. Remember that observations are perceived with one of your senses and inferences are the explanations you pose to explain your observations. Your observations may also raise a lot of questions, be sure to note these in your lab notebook.

Place several termites in the center of each circle, and observe for several minutes. The best way to move the organisms from one location to another is to gently brush them with the paintbrush. Record your observations and inferences or questions in the appropriate columns. After you have recorded your observations, draw a second set of two circles similar to the first but use the remaining blue and black pens. Be careful that none of the circles overlap. You may want to make a second container for your second set of circles.

Record your observations in your lab notebook, discuss the significance of your observations within your group, and generate some testable hypotheses to explain your observations. After the group discusses the observations, use the remaining materials and try some simple experiments to see if the data you collect support your hypotheses.

CHAPTER 2 REVIEW QUESTIONS (5 POINTS EACH)

Name_____

1.   What was the variable that attracted the termites?

2.   Briefly describe what your group did to test your hypothesis.

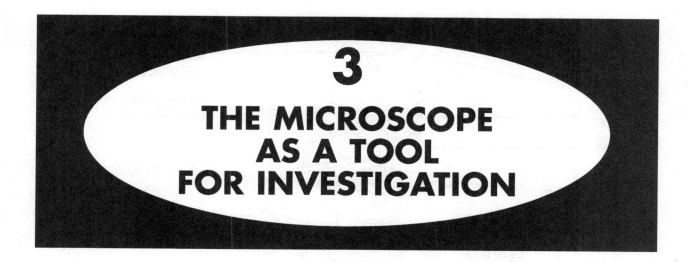

OBJECTIVES

Learn the basic care and handling of a compound microscope.

Use the microscope to investigate a community of your choice.

BACKGROUND

With this exercise you will use a compound microscope to make some observations about the living world. The microscope is a very powerful tool for observing organisms that are too small for the naked eye to see. You can find a diagram of the compound microscope in your lab manual. Be sure you are able to identify the major parts.

MATERIALS FOR ONE GROUP

1 compound microscope
Plain glass slides
Coverslips
Tap water (dropper)
Prepared slides

PROCEDURE

Obtain a microscope; your instructor will show you where they are.

Always carry the microscope with two hands.

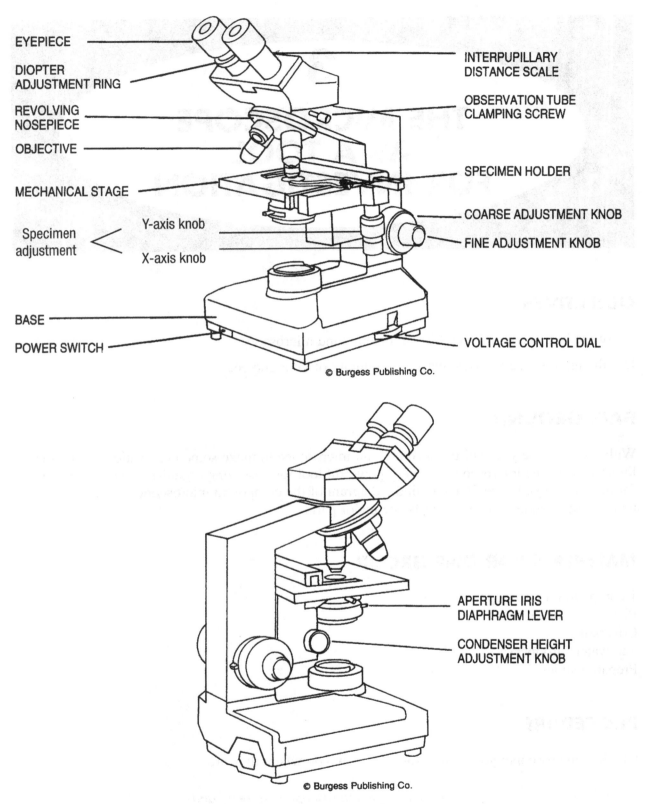

EYEPIECE

DIOPTER ADJUSTMENT RING

REVOLVING NOSEPIECE

OBJECTIVE

MECHANICAL STAGE

Specimen adjustment
Y-axis knob
X-axis knob

BASE

POWER SWITCH

INTERPUPILLARY DISTANCE SCALE

OBSERVATION TUBE CLAMPING SCREW

SPECIMEN HOLDER

COARSE ADJUSTMENT KNOB

FINE ADJUSTMENT KNOB

VOLTAGE CONTROL DIAL

© Burgess Publishing Co.

APERTURE IRIS DIAPHRAGM LEVER

CONDENSER HEIGHT ADJUSTMENT KNOB

© Burgess Publishing Co.

FIGURE 1. Typical Compound Microscope

Plug the microscope into an electrical outlet and turn on the light. The microscope consists of a system of optics and focusing controls.

At the top of the scope is the **ocular lens** or (eyepiece). This particular lens will make the image appear 10 times larger than life (this is usually abbreviated 10X).

At the bottom of the body of the scope is a revolving set of lenses that screw into the nosepiece. These are called **objective lenses.** Turn the nosepiece until you hear a clicking sound; the objective lens is now centered in the light path of the microscope.

Always, always, always, and we mean *always,* start on low power! This will be denoted as a 4X on the objective lens. Remember that the eyepiece lens is a 10X . We're looking through two sets of lenses; we must multiply the magnification of one lens by the other. Therefore, 40X life size is the total magnification power on the lowest setting.

On each side of the microscope you will notice 2 focusing knobs. The outer (largest knob) is the coarse focus, the inner (smaller) knob is the fine focus. With your microscope set up on a low-power, place a prepared slide of the organism of your choice under the objective lens and on the flat portion known as the stage. Many microscope stages move so that the slide may be locked-on and moved around in a precise manner. Please note the method in which the slide is held on the stage of these microscopes.

Obtain from your instructor a prepared slide of the organism of your choice from those available. Taking a careful look at your specimen, draw a picture in your lab notebook of what you see with the naked eye. Now use the microscope on low power and draw what you see in your field of view.

Now you're ready to go up to the next higher power, this will be a 10X objective. How did the field of view change? Is your view still in focus? If it is not, use the **fine focus knob** to bring the image into sharp focus. **Use the fine focus knob only** to adjust the focus once you are at higher powers! When using a microscope, always focus first on low power and then incrementally increase the power. Hopefully our microscopes are set up to be parafocal. This means that each lens has the same focal plane in your sample. This rarely happens, but will require only fine adjustment using that fine focus knob. **Never, ever, ever use the coarse focus knob once you have gone above low power!** If you remember this simple rule, the chance of you smashing the objective into the slide will be greatly reduced! The slides aren't cheap and the lenses are even less cheap. Be careful.

Underneath the microscope stage is a set of optics known as the condenser. This helps focus the light beam directly on our sample. Part of this assembly is a lever that you will want to get to know; it controls the **iris diaphragm.** This diaphragm will constrict the beam of light passing through your sample and help to eliminate glare. Glare is a microscopist's worst enemy. Eliminating glare will allow us to improve contrast in and see our sample more clearly.

Draw a picture in your lab notebook of the organism you have chosen now magnified 100X. How is this image different from your drawing at 40X times magnification?

With your samples sharply in focus, turn the nosepiece to the next objective and examine your sample at high power! This objective lens is marked 40X; you are now viewing your sample at 400 times the magnification of your naked eye!

How did the image change?

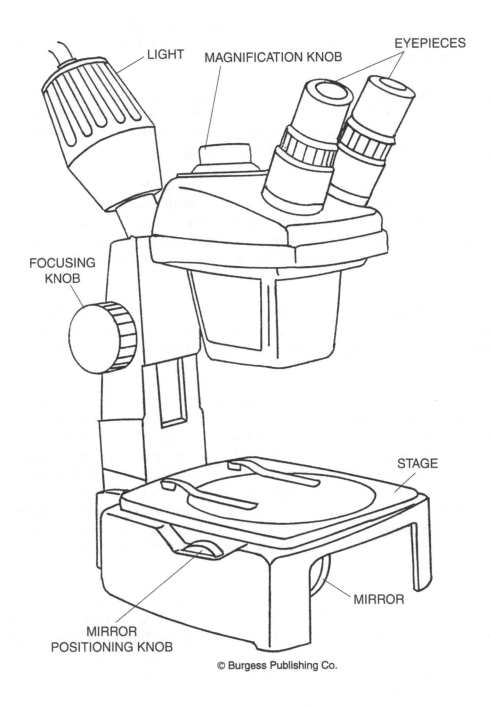

© Burgess Publishing Co.

Below is a list of microscope parts that will be important for you to know for proper use of a compound microscope. Note the magnification of each objective and the order they are in on the revolving nosepiece. This may vary depending on the microscope. Also, when using the 100X objective immersion oil must be used.

Record the magnification for each objective (and ocular)

Ocular _____   Scanning objective _____   Low power objective _____
High power objective _____   Oil immersion objective _____

PART	DESCRIPTION
Ocular	eyepiece; part you look through
Body tube	metal tube between ocular and objectives
Objectives	lenses found at the lower end of the body tube; on rotating nosepiece
Arm	metal part of the scope which attach body tube to base; coarse adjustment knob located on arm; one hand placed here when carrying microscope
Coarse adjustment knob	used to bring object into focus when using low power Objective
Fine adjustment knob	used to fine tune focusing and whenever high power or oil immersion objectives are being used
Stage	where microscope slide is placed for viewing; mechanical stage is movable and usually has one knob to control vertical movement and one knob to control horizontal movement
Stage clips	hold microscope slide in place
Condenser	focuses the light source on the specimen
Iris diaphragm	controls contrast and definition; controls image quality; used to increase contrast when viewing unstained specimens
Condenser adjustment knob	used to move condenser up and down
Base	portion on which microscope sits; one hand should be paced here when carrying the microscope

You will be using two types of microscopes in this lab the **compound** and **dissecting** microscopes. The compound microscope is capable of the highest magnification. It is designed to view specimens that are not visible to the naked eye. In order for light to pass through a specimen so it will be visible the specimen must be prepared very thin. Dissecting microscopes are designed to view details on much larger specimens and to give a three dimensional image. Microscopes which have only one ocular are monocular scopes while those that have two oculars are binocular scopes. All microscopes used in this lab will be binocular scopes.

ORIENTATION OF THE SPECIMEN

In this activity you will practice skills required to load a slide on the stage along with orientation of the specimen using the X and Y adjustment knobs. The combination of lenses and lights used in a typical compound light microscope do more than magnifying the specimen you are viewing.

1.   Obtain a microscope slide on which the letter **e** has been mounted.
2.   Hold slide so the **e** is in normal reading position.
3.   Secure slide using stage clips.
4.   Center the letter in the stage before looking through the oculars.
5.   View the letter under low power objective.
6.   Use the course adjustment knob and focus upward until the letter comes in focus.
7.   Use the fine adjustment knob to fine tune the focus.
8.   Without changing the focus, carefully rotate the objectives to bring the 10X objective in place. Listen or feel for a click to make sure the objectives are in the correct position. Is the letter still in focus? This occurs because most microscopes are **parfocal;** meaning you can change from one objective to another without losing focus.

Answer the following questions in your laboratory notebook;

1.   What two things does the microscope do to the letter **e**?

2.   Slowly move the slide to the right. What direction does the letter move?

3.   Slowly move the slide to the left. What direction does the letter move?

4.   Move the slide away from you. What happen to the letter?

5.   In what direction would you have to move the letter to make the image of the **e** appear to move up and to the right?

6.   Does the brightness of the viewing area increase or decrease as you go from lowest power to the highest power (43X)?

USING THE MICROSCOPE TO TEST A HYPOTHESIS

Have you ever wondered about pond scum? Lord knows I have on any number of occasions. What kinds of organisms do you suppose make up your run-of-the-mill pond scum? Ever wondered about this? This is the kind of thing that many biologists wonder about. This is a perfect hypothesis to test using a microscope as a tool to explore the world of pond scum. Set up around the classroom will be a number of different types of "ponds." There may be some freshly collected pond water, a grass infusion, a fish tank, maybe even a salt-water aquarium. Ever wonder what that slimy stuff growing in your fish tank was? Let's find out!

But first, we must develop a hypothesis. Would you expect to find microscopic algae? Microscopic animals? Little itty-bitty Green Men? What will be the dominant life forms? What will be the rare life forms? Even if you have never seen a sample of pond water before, what would you expect to see? Write down your hypothesis then use the microscope as a tool to test the hypothesis. Gently, take a cotton swab and "sample" some of the material floating in these ponds or attached to the sides of the containers. Gently roll the swab on the center of a clean microscope slide and add a coverslip. Starting on the lowest power, what do you see? You may need to add a drop of fresh water and maybe a drop of proto-slow to slow down the swimmers.

In your lab notebook draw a picture of the organisms you found in the community you have sampled. Now test your hypothesis by viewing, then draw as many different components of this community as you can. Which organisms do you find the most of? Which organisms do you find only infrequently? Your lab instructor will have diagrams of some of the most common pond scum organisms as a reference. Are there organisms here you have never seen before? I bet you never thought there was this kind of biological diversity in a tiny little drop of water.

We will use algae and some other microorganisms for various studies later in the term. Now would be an excellent time for you to begin some background research on the kinds of organisms that are commonly found in freshwater environments. These will serve as model organisms for our ecological studies that we will begin in the coming weeks.

ALGAE

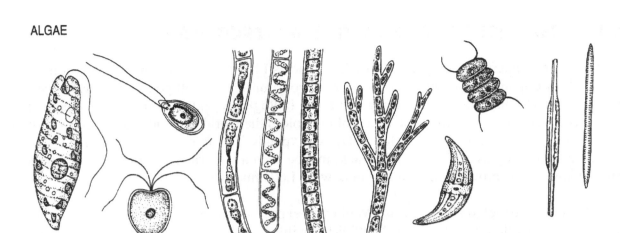

PROTOZOANS

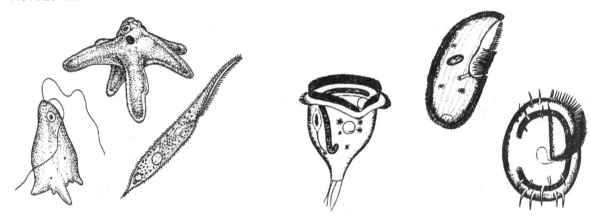

MULTICELLULAR ANIMALS

GASTROTRICHS   ROTIFERS   CRUSTACEANS

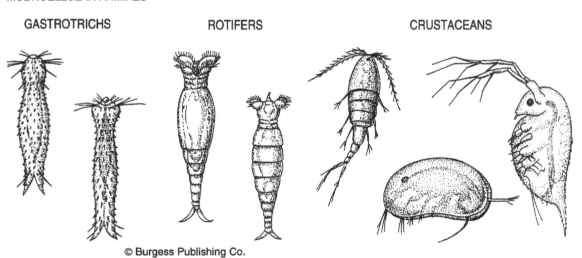

SOME COMMON ORGANISMS FOUND IN POND WATER

CHAPTER 3 REVIEW QUESTIONS (2 POINTS EACH)

Name_____

1. What were the two types of microscopes studied in lab today?

2. Which of these two types of microscopes is used to view specimens that are
    not visible to the naked eye?

3. Which objective do you start with when bring your specimen in initial focus?

4. Where are the objectives found on a compound microscope?

5. Which adjustment knob is used when you are bring a specimen in focus
    when the high power objective is being used?

4
ENVIRONMENTAL POLLUTION CONTROL

OBJECTIVES

Develop problem-solving skills.

Use a spectrophotometer to analyze a sample.

BACKGROUND INFORMATION

You are a member of a team of environmental pollution control experts. You work for an industrial firm that makes copper plates components of sophisticated electrical equipment. A by-product of this process is a solution that contains very high concentrations of copper in the form of a copper sulfate (or copper chloride) solution. Because copper at high concentrations is toxic to many aquatic organisms, your firm has been told that it cannot discharge effluent into the nearby water system at concentrations of copper greater than 5ppm. The waste copper solution that is produced by the process your firm uses is much higher than that. Your team has been provided a stock solution of copper that contains 50,000ppm copper to use to develop a process for accurately determining the concentration of copper in the waste effluent before it is discharged. It is critical for the firm to have a monitoring procedure in place to make sure that any effluent discharged meets environmental safety standards of no more than 5ppm copper. You must develop a procedure for determining the concentration of copper in effluent, test your procedure, and confirm the accuracy of the procedure by successfully determining the concentration of copper in stock solutions provided by the company for which you do not know the concentration.

MATERIALS FOR ONE GROUP

Test tube rack
Test tubes
Test solutions (see your lab instructor)
1, 2, 5, and 10ml pipettes and pumps
Spectrophotometers

PROCEDURE

A good strategy for solving a problem like this is to:
1. Clearly define the problem (What are you supposed to do?)
2. List all the information you have about the problem (what you know, what you have available to work with, what you have to find out).
3. Generate and consider alternative ways to solve the problem, and materials you will require.
4. Design a plan for solving the problem.
5. Try out your plan.
6. Evaluate the success of your approach; if necessary, modify the procedure and try again.

THINGS TO CONSIDER

Notice the color of the solution. Your instructor will demonstrate a very powerful tool for measuring the concentrations of compound (and even organisms) in a solution. Is there a way that you can systematically change the concentration of a solution? What do you have to have before you can determine the concentration of an unknown?

CHAPTER 4 REVIEW QUESTIONS (5 POINTS EACH)

Name_____

1. Describe the pipetting technique used in this activity.

2. What was the approximate concentration of the unknown solution?

5
ENVIRONMENTAL POLLUTION

OBJECTIVES

Develop and test a hypothesis that applies to real world environmental issues.

Use sophisticated tools for collecting scientific data.

Analyze and interpret real scientific data.

BACKGROUND INFORMATION

Water supplies, both fresh and marine, may be polluted by a variety of materials potentially dangerous to plants and other organisms. Because it is not practical to test polluting compounds on humans or other complex organisms to determine the organisms' response to toxic levels of these materials, scientists often must use an indicator organism to give them some idea of the concentration of various pollutants in water supplies. Information about the health and behavior of indicator organisms that have been exposed to pollutants can then be extrapolated to predict the effects of pollutants on other members of the ecosystem.

In this exercise, your group will design an experiment to test the effects of some toxins on algae, an aquatic organism that will serve as an indicator organism. After you run your experiment and collect the data, you will prepare a formal lab report (format and instructions for the report will be provided today in class). Some library work and a web-based search will aid you in this task. Ecological characteristics of your algae and some of the properties of your pollutant will be necessary for your paper.

A WORD ABOUT PLAGIARISM

Plagiarism is defined by the *American College Dictionary* as: "Copying or imitating the language, ideas, and thoughts of another author and passing off that writing as one's original work." This includes "Cut and Paste" from a web site or other electronic document. Always use proper citation formats when using material from another author. See the grading rubric and sample lab report in this manual.

It is necessary for your group to work as a team to design and execute the experiment, collect the data, and even analyze it. HOWEVER, EACH MEMBER OF THE GROUP WILL WRITE HIS/HER OWN PAPER! **Failing to do this is grounds for a failing (F) grade in the course.**

MATERIALS FOR ONE GROUP

1 test tube rack
12 screw cap test tubes with caps
Ankistrodesmus stock cultures
Alga-Gro™ nutrient media
A pollutant (see your lab instructor)
1, 2, and 5 ml pipettes and pumps
Spectrophotometers

PROCEDURE

Your lab instructor will organize you into groups of three or four students. The alga *Ankistrodesmus* is your experimental organism. Algae are aquatic organisms that are classified in the Kingdom Protista. Some algae are commonly found in polluted water, while others are not. This part of your library/internet assignment to determine in what kind of a habitat *Ankistrodesmus* is usually found.

All algae are photosynthetic organisms, requiring light and basic inorganic nutrients for growth. Light will be provided for the algae by a light bank in the classroom. Your group will now design an experiment as you wish within the following guidelines:

Several pollutants will be available. These will all be common constituents of agricultural fertilizers or other chemicals commonly used throughout the nation on household and/or industrial scales. Your group needs to pick **one.** Each group should plan to set up 4 culture tubes, each containing a similar number (population) of algae cells and similar volumes of liquid (5 ml of starter solution with algae). Each tube should be clearly labeled with the group's name, section number and the treatment the algae will be receiving. One group should have no treatment at all. Why is this? To the untreated tube, add a second 5ml of fresh **Alga-GroTM** medium to give a total volume of 10 ml. For each of the remaining three tubes, you need to decide on the concentration for the treatment and calculate how much of your selected pollutant and **Alga-GroTM** you need to add to each tube to achieve a final volume of 10 ml and the desired concentration of pollutant. For example, the fertilizer is provided to you as a 100 percent solution. If you add 5 ml of this solution to 5ml of *Ankistrodesmus* starter suspension, you have diluted the fertilizer by one half; the algae are now suspended in a 50% fertilizer solution. Your group needs to decide on, calculate, and prepare three different treatments levels of your pollutant. Prepare duplicate tubes (replicates) at each treatment level. Why do we need duplicate tubes?

You now must obtain an estimate of the number of cells present in each culture tube so you have a starting point for measuring growth or lack of growth in your samples. We could count the cells directly, but there is a much quicker, more indirect way using the spectrophotometer.

Swirl or otherwise agitate the tube containing your sample so that the cells seem to be evenly distributed in the tube.

Your instructor will show you how to blank the spectrophotometer using a tube of fresh **Alga-Gro™** media. The blank is a tool to calibrate the machine so that the optical density we read is that of the algae cells not the **Alga-Gro™**. Once the machine is calibrated, read both of your control replicates; the units for this measurement will be Optical Density. Now you will need to re-blank the spec. How do we do this?? What will you use? How many blank tubes will you need?

Stop now and discuss this with your group.

After you have blanked the spectrophotometer, read both replicates and proceed to the next blank. ENTER ALL DATA IN YOUR LAB NOTEBOOK.

Create a table like this one:

	Baseline (Day 0) O.D.	Day 3 O.D.	Day 7 O.D.	Day 11 O.D.	Day 14 O.D.	Net Gain/Loss O.D. (Day 14 O.D.–Day 0 O.D.)
Control A						
Control B						
Trt. 1A						
Trt. 1B						
Trt. 2A						
Trt. 2B						
Trt. 3A						
Trt. 3B						

If you have measured your volumes precisely and accurately, all of the entries in the day 0 column should be the same (or very close). Why is this? Talk it over with your group.

The algae will be allowed to grow for the next 2 weeks. You will need to coordinate with your group a time when all of you can come back 3–4 days from now (yes, we know this will not be your regular class time) to take a reading. Reading 3 will be taken during your next scheduled lab meeting, reading 4 will be taken 3–4 days after that, and the final reading will be made during the next regularly scheduled lab time. Why do we need to take multiple data points?

TIMES THE LAB WILL BE OPEN WILL BE POSTED ON THE DOOR. IF ANOTHER LAB IS IN SESSION, THEY HAVE FIRST USE OF THE EQUIPMENT. IF YOU ARE QUIET AND THE EQUIPMENT IS NOT IN USE, YOU MAY COME IN AND COLLECT YOUR DATA.

After you have collected 2 weeks worth of data, subtract the OD from day 0 from the OD from day 14. Do this for both sets of replicates.

Now average the values for both sets of replicates. Why do we average our replicates?

$$\frac{(Net\ Gain\ or\ Loss\ OD\ rep\ A) + (Net\ Gain\ or\ Loss\ O.D.\ rep\ B)}{2} = Average\ Net\ Gain\ or\ Loss\ O.D.$$

Record your data in your lab notebook in a table like the one below.

Treatment	Average Net Gain or Loss O.D.
Control	
Trt. 1	
Trt.2	
Trt.3	

THINGS TO CONSIDER

What is happening when the Optical Density of the treatment group is increasing?

What is happening when the Optical Density of the treatment group is decreasing?

CHAPTER 5 REVIEW QUESTIONS (2 POINTS EACH)

Name_____

1.   What are the two locations your tubes are place in?

2.   What were the two different pollutants that could be used in this activity?

3.   A _____ was used to measure the activity in
      each tube.

4.   How many replications are set up at each concentration of the algae plus
      pollutant?

5.   How many replications are used in the blank tubes?

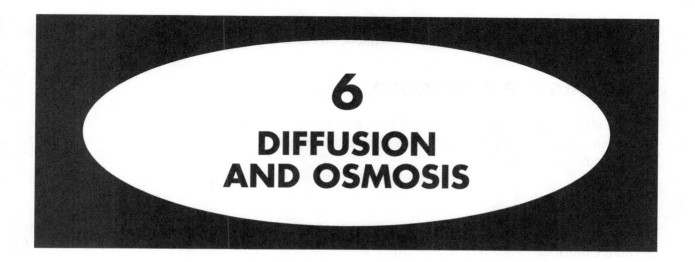

6
DIFFUSION AND OSMOSIS

OBJECTIVES

Explain the processes of diffusion and osmosis at the molecular level.

Describe the role that osmosis plays in maintaining life at the cellular and organismal levels.

BACKGROUND INFORMATION

All atoms and molecules are in constant motion except at absolute zero. Heat is the energy source that drives the random collisions of these particles; the higher the temperature, the faster the particles move and the greater the energy with which they impact and rebound. As a result of random collisions, atoms and molecules tend to move from regions of higher concentration to regions of lower concentration through a process called diffusion. This behavior of atoms and molecules has a major impact on the way living systems function. Water is the medium that serves as the basis for life as we know it. The cells of any living system must exchange nutrients, gases, waste products, etc. with the aqueous environment around them. These exchanges occur as atoms and molecules diffuse from areas of higher to areas of lower concentration. Osmosis is a special case of diffusion in which water moves across a differentially permeable membrane (such as a cell membrane) from an area of higher to an area of lower concentration.

The cheeseburger you had for lunch and that is residing in your small intestines is diffusing right now. The components of that cheeseburger are higher inside your small intestine than in the blood circulating through the capillaries that lie beneath cells lining the small intestine. The molecules that made up that cheeseburger (carbohydrates, amino acids, and lipids) and that have been broken down by the digestive process are now diffusing into your blood. If this process did not work, our cells would not be able to absorb nutrients or excrete waste products and life, as we know it, would not be possible. The air in your lungs contains nitrogen, oxygen, and carbon dioxide (and a few other trace gases). As you inhale, the concentration of oxygen in the air in your lungs is higher than the concentration of oxygen carried by your blood; oxygen diffuses from your lungs into your blood. Carbon dioxide (a waste product of cellular respiration) is at a higher concentration in your blood than in your lungs. Carbon dioxide diffuses out of the blood and into your lungs as it moves from an area of higher to an area of lower concentration. Again life as we know it would not be possible without this fundamental process.

MATERIALS FOR ONE GROUP

Various diffusion displays (see your lab instructor)
Unknown sucrose solution (see your lab instructor)
Dialysis tubing and string
Small funnels
Slides and cover slips
India ink
Balances
Sodium Chloride
Potatoes
Beakers

PROCEDURE

EXERCISE #1 DIFFUSION

This experiment will be set up in front of the class. At some point during today's class observe the experiments at the front of the lab. Some potassium permanganate crystals were dropped into one of the test tubes. As these crystals dissolve you'll see a purple color migrate through the water column. Your lab instructor will start this demonstration at the beginning of the period. Please take a look at it several times throughout the class and notice any color change in the water in the test tube.

A second test tube contains two layers. The bottom layer is a super saturated copper sulfate solution; the top layer is pure water. A supersaturated solution contains the maximum amount of a given compound that can be held in solution without a solid precipitate forming. If possible, demonstration tubes will be set up a week in advance, three days in advance, and the day of your class so that you may see the diffusion of this particular compound over a period of several days. Describe what you observe in each tube. What changes occur over time? Explain what is happening at the molecular level. Is there a way you could speed up this process? Justify your answer.

EXERCISE #2 DIFFUSION IN ACTION, BROWNIAN MOVEMENT

Place a drop of distilled water on a microscope slide and to it add a drop of India ink. Cover the drop with a coverslip and observe with a compound microscope. Begin with lowest power and slowly increase the magnification until you can see the tiny black specks of carbon that make up the black pigment in the ink. Being very careful not to bump the table or the microscope, observe these small specks for a few moments and notice the random motion of the tiniest ones. The motion is caused by the heat from the lamp under the stage of your microscope causing the water molecules to bump into the tiny particles of carbon. This process is called Brownian movement after the 18th century physician who first described it.

EXERCISE #3 USING OSMOSIS TO DETERMINE
AN UNKNOWN CONCENTRATION

Osmosis is a special case of diffusion in which water moves across a semi-permeable membrane. Imagine a membrane that has properties similar to a colander. When you dump that pot of boiling water and spaghetti into a colander, the spaghetti stays behind but the water is free to move through the little tiny holes. Imagine this same sort of process on a molecular scale. Surrounding each one of your cells is a membrane across which water passes freely, but through which large molecules such as sucrose and ions such as sodium and chloride cannot simply diffuse. Because of the processes of diffusion and osmosis, both living and non-living systems tend to reach a state of equilibrium. Equilibrium in this instance can be defined as a state of balance where there is just as much of a particular compound on one side of the membrane as on the other. For this experiment we will use dialysis tubing to simulate a cell membrane. This tubing is essentially a microscopic sieve across which water can pass, however larger molecules such as sucrose cannot.

Cut five 12.5 cm (5 in) strips of dialysis tubing being careful not to puncture the tubing. In a small beaker place cold water and soak your strips of dialysis tubing so that they become flexible. Remove the strips of tubing from the water and use the string provided to tie off one end of the tubing to make a small pouch. Into each pouch you will put 15ml of a sucrose solution. Prepare a series of sucrose solutions at concentrations of 5%, 10%, 15%, and 20%. To prepare the 5% sucrose solution, add 5 g of sucrose to 95 g (milliliters) of water. Prepare 100 ml of each of the remaining solutions in a similar manner. Add 15 ml of each of the four sucrose concentrations into separate dialysis bags. Your instructor will assign your group an unknown sucrose solution to be placed in the fifth dialysis bag.

FOLD TOP OVER, SQUEEZE OUT
AIR, AND TIE SECURELY WITH
STRING.

Tie the open ends of the dialysis bags closed with string to form little sausages. Be careful to squeeze as much air out of the dialysis bags as possible, but leave a little slack in the tube to allow for expansion. Weigh each sausage to the nearest 0.01 g then carefully lower all five dialysis bags into beakers of deionized water at exactly the same time. Every 15 minutes for the next 90 minutes remove each sausage and weigh it carefully, noting the net gain or loss of water by subtracting the weight of the bag at time zero from the weight of the bag at each sampling period. Record your data in your lab notebook in a table.

Now graph the net weight gain or loss during the 90 minutes for your unknown and each known sucrose concentration. In your lab notebook, interpret your graph in a few sentences.

THINGS TO CONSIDER

What kind of pattern, if any, did you see?

How can you use your data to help you determine what the concentration of your unknown sucrose solution is?

What is the concentration of your unknown solution? Justify your answer.

Did any of your dialysis bags lose weight?

What does it mean if your dialysis bag lost weight?

Compare your data with that of your classmates.

EXERCISE #4 OSMOSIS AND LIVING CELLS

Obtain a tuber (the fancy term for a potato) and carefully cut nine, 1cm^3 pieces. Keep the pieces as uniform in size as possible. Divide the cubes into 3 groups of 3 and weigh each group to the nearest 0.01 g. Obtain three beakers. To the first beaker add 200 ml of deionized water, to the second add 200 ml of a 0.10% sodium chloride solution, and to the third add 200 ml of a 3% sodium chloride solution.

At time zero, drop each group of three potato cubes into one of the beakers. Weigh each treatment group every 15 minutes for one hour, blotting the surface dry before each weighing. Enter your data in your lab notebook in a table. Compare the net change in weight of each treatment sample by subtracting the weight at times zero from the weight of the treatment group at the final weighing. Graph the net change in weight for each treatment group.

THINGS TO CONSIDER

Which of the three solutions was closest to the natural tonicity of the potato cells? Use data to justify your answer.

CHAPTER 6 REVIEW QUESTIONS (10 POINTS)

Name_____

1.　　What pattern did you observe in Exercise 3 using osmosis to determine an unknown concentration? (what happened to the weight of the dialysis bags in relation to the concentration of sucrose)

7
ENZYME ACTIVITY

OBJECTIVES

Describe the function of a common organic catalyst (catalase).

List various factors that affect the performance of catalase; explain why these factors affect enzyme performance.

Use two different methods to measure catalase activity. Compare and contrast the two methods.

BACKGROUND INFORMATION

Enzymes are organic catalysts. That is, they are molecules made by living systems that speed up reactions without being consumed in the reaction. Enzymes catalyze virtually all of the chemical reactions that occur in living systems; an understanding of enzymes and how they work is necessary to an understanding of life.

In general, a separate enzyme catalyzes each metabolic reaction. An enzyme has a highly specific active site that interacts with the substrate and facilitates the reaction to generate the products. The fit of the substrate to the enzyme has often been likened to a key in a lock. The wrong key, even if the difference is minor, will not open the lock. Similarly, an enzyme will not usually work with the wrong substrate.

Enzymes are remarkably efficient catalysts. Under optimum conditions, an enzyme can convert substrate to product at a rate of about 1000 molecules per/sec. Optimum conditions depend on the enzyme and the organism from which it comes. Any aspect of the environment may affect the activity of the enzyme. The most critical factors are usually pH, temperature, substrate concentration, and the concentration of the enzyme. Your lab instructor may take some time to discuss how and why each of these factors affects enzyme activity.

Scientists often use more than one technique to study the same natural phenomenon. Today we're going to use two different experimental techniques to study the effect of some environmental variables on the functioning of the enzyme catalase. Catalase is a widely distributed enzyme that can be isolated from many different plant and animal sources. Catalase degrades hydrogen peroxide (H_2O_2), a metabolic waste product that can become toxic at high levels, into water and oxygen.

$$2H_2O_2 \xrightarrow[\text{CATALASE}]{\text{HEAT}} 2H_2O + O_2$$

In biochemical terms, hydrogen peroxide is the substrate of the enzyme; its products are H_2O and O_2. We will use potatoes as the source of this enzyme, but it is found in many different places including your blood.

Each group will be assigned a procedure to follow and a variable to test such as substrate concentration, or enzyme concentration.

MATERIALS FOR ONE GROUP

Potatoes
Deionized water
Ice and bucket
3% H_2O_2
Beakers
Blender
Strainer
Additional (Method 1)
O_2 capture apparatus
Additional (Method 2)
Glass fiber discs
Beakers
Forceps

PROCEDURE

To prepare your enzyme's stock solution, peel 85 g of potato and cut into half-inch pieces. Place the potato in a blender with 120 ml of deionized water. Homogenize the tissue for 30 seconds at full speed.

Next, filter this potato margarita through four layers of cheesecloth into a small beaker that is set in an ice bucket. Let the filtrate stand for three minutes to allow the starch granules to settle out. This is your catalase (100%) stock solution.

METHOD #1

EFFECT OF ENZYME CONCENTRATION

Place 10ml of 100% catalase solution into a reaction flask. Pipette 3ml of the 3% hydrogen peroxide solution into the plastic test-tube cap and lower the cap into the flask without mixing the two solutions.

Place the stopper on the reaction flask and insert the glass tube at the end of the rubber tubing into the open end of an inverted 100ml burette. Submerge the open end of the burette with tubing inserted in a container of water. Using the straw mouthpiece attached to the tip of the burette, draw water up into the burette to the 0ml mark and clamp off the tube (see Figure 1).

At time zero, shake the reaction flask to upset the cap and mix the H_2O_2 with the enzyme. Shake the flask continuously until no more bubbles are produced; this usually takes less than 3 minutes. O_2 gas will collect at the top of the burette as the reaction proceeds. Measure the amount of oxygen, in ml, that has been produced by the reaction by determining the number of ml of water that has been displaced. Do two more replicates at this enzyme concentration. Now dilute your catalase stock solutions for three replicates at 50% (keep the total volume the same) so you would use 5ml catalase stock and 5 ml water. Now run 3 replicates at 25% catalase. Do you notice anything different about the reaction?

EFFECT OF SUBSTRATE CONCENTRATION

In this experiment you will use the 100% catalase preparation in all reaction flasks and will vary the substrate (H_2O_2) concentration to determine the effect on enzyme activity. Repeat the procedure described above. Run three replicates at each of three H_2O_2 concentrations—3%, 1.5%, and 0.75%.

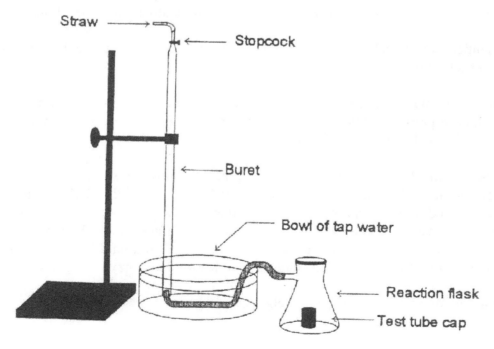

FIGURE 1. Set-up for the catalase assay

Prepare a table such as this in your lab notebook.

Enzyme Concentration ($H_2O_2 = 3\%$)	100% catalase	50% catalase	25% catalase
Rep. 1	mlO_2	mlO_2	mlO_2
Rep. 2	mlO_2	mlO_2	mlO_2
Rep. 3	mlO_2	mlO_2	mlO_2
AVERAGE	mlO_2	mlO_2	mlO_2

Substrate Concentration (Catalase = 100%)	3% H_2O_2	1.5% H_2O_2	0.75% H_2O_2
Rep. 1	mlO_2	mlO_2	mlO_2
Rep. 2	mlO_2	mlO_2	mlO_2
Rep. 3	mlO_2	mlO_2	mlO_2
AVERAGE	mlO_2	mlO_2	mlO_2

METHOD #2

Label three 50ml beakers as follows: 100%, 50% and 25% enzyme and prepare 40 ml of cata-lase solution at each of the above concentrations. (Remember your catalase stock solution is @100%, so 40ml of a 50% solution would be 20ml catalase stock plus 20ml H_2O.)

Label an identical set of beakers for the substrate. Place 40 ml of 3% percent hydrogen peroxide solution into each of the beakers.

Using a forceps, immerse a glass fiber filter disk to half its diameter in the first of the catalase solutions you have prepared. Allow the disk to absorb the enzyme solution for 5 seconds, remove and drain for 10 seconds on a paper towel.

Drop the disc saturated with enzyme solution into the first substrate solution. The disk will sink to the bottom of the beaker. As O_2 is produced in the breakdown of the H_2O_2 by catalase, the gas will become trapped in the fibers of the disc. When enough oxygen has collected in the disk to lower its overall density, the disk will float to the surface of the solution. Record the time in sec-onds from the moment the disk first touches the substrate solution until it floats to the surface of the substrate solution. Repeat the procedure three times for each enzyme concentration.

Record your data in a table in your lab notebook.

Enzyme Concentration ($H_2O_2 = 3\%$)	100% catalase	50% catalase	25% catalase
Rep. 1	Sec.	Sec.	Sec.
Rep. 2	Sec.	Sec.	Sec.
Rep. 3	Sec.	Sec.	Sec.
AVERAGE	Sec.	Sec.	Sec.

Now repeat the procedure above, but vary the H2O2 (substrate) and keep the enzyme concentration constant (100% catalase). The initial concentration of the H2O2 is 3%.

Substrate Concentration (Catalase = 100%)	3% H_2O_2	1.5% H_2O_2	0.75% H_2O_2
Rep. 1	Sec.	Sec.	Sec.
Rep. 2	Sec.	Sec.	Sec.
Rep. 3	Sec.	Sec.	Sec.
AVERAGE	Sec.	Sec.	Sec.

Record the data you have collected on the board. Graph the class data and compare the two methods of determining the effect of substrate concentration or enzyme concentration on enzyme activity.

THINGS TO CONSIDER

(Discuss with the class)
Did varying the substrate concentration or the enzyme concentration have the greatest effect on the enzyme's activity? Is this what your group expected? What do these results tell you about the nature of catalase? Do the same trends in the data appear when different techniques were used?

THINGS TO CONSIDER FOR FUTURE LABS

(or maybe your independent study project)
What other factors can affect catalase activity? Will either technique for determining enzyme activity work equally well for any factor you plan to study? Why or why not? These are questions you will want to consider as you design your independent research investigation.

CHAPTER 7 REVIEW QUESTIONS (2 POINTS EACH)

Name _____

1.   Was more oxygen produced when enzyme concentration was high or low?

2.   Was more oxygen produced when substrate concentration was high or low?

3.   Was more oxygen produced when the enzyme concentration was varied or the substrate concentration?

4.   What was the enzyme stock solution made from?

5.   What was the gas that was collected at the top of the buret?

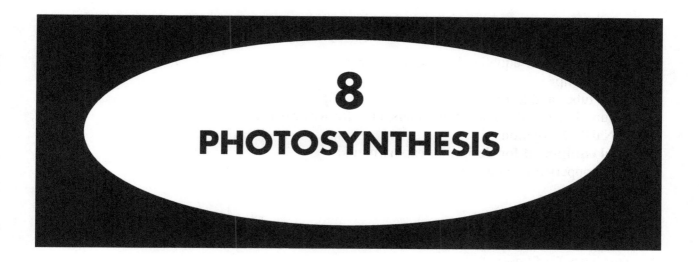

OBJECTIVES

Use a variety of tools to explore photosynthesis in a green plant.

Design and conduct a well controlled experiment to study photosynthesis in a green plant.

Be able to explain the effect of varying environmental conditions such as light, carbon dioxide concentration, temperature, etc., on photosynthesis and justify their explanations with data they have collected.

BACKGROUND INFORMATION

Life on earth is almost entirely solar powered. Photosynthesis, the process by which plants make food molecules from carbon dioxide and water in the presence of light, is the most important chemical process on Earth because it provides the food supply for virtually all organisms—plants, animals, protists, fungi, and bacteria. And don't forget that you are included in this group.

In this laboratory you will examine the process of photosynthesis, determine what conditions affect the rate at which photosynthesis occurs, and consider the implications that the changing environmental conditions on earth have for the process of photosynthesis.

The general overall occasion for photosynthesis in green plants is:

$$6CO_2 + 6H_2O \xrightarrow[Chlorophyll]{Light} C_6H_{12}O_6 + 6O_2$$

Through this process green plants transform solar energy into chemical energy, build their bodies out of air, replace atmospheric oxygen, and provide food that serves as a usable energy source for the rest of the living world. The same plant material is the ultimate source of the atoms and molecules that make up all other organisms.

MATERIALS FOR ONE GROUP

Elodea, a fresh water aquatic plant (several sprigs)
1 100-watt lamp
Large test tubes and test tube rack
1 aquarium, large beakers, large glass jars, etc., for water barrier
0.25% $NaHCO_3$ solution
Optional equipment for designing experiments:
8 rubber stoppers for test tubes
Food coloring
pH meters
Ice
$NaHCO_3$
Acetate sheets for filters

In this lab you are on your own to design and carry out an experiment that will provide data about the process of photosynthesis in *Elodea,* an aquatic plant. Use the following procedure as the basis for your experiment. Record your experimental design and your data in your lab notebook. Be prepared to present your experimental design, your data, and your conclusions by the end of the class period.

PROCEDURE

In the diagram on page 9–45 sprigs of *Elodea* are inverted inside a large test tube and immersed in a solution of 0.25% $NaHCO_3$. Before completely immersing the *Elodea,* 2-3 mm of the end of the stem opposite the growing point is cut off using a scalpel. Care is taken to ensure that the cut end of the *Elodea* sprig is below the surface of the liquid. Test tube racks or Erlenmeyer flask can be used to hold the tubes erect and tubes are sealed using rubber stoppers. Measurement will be taken using pH meter during the course of the experiment.

Work with your laboratory group to design an experiment that will provide additional data about the effect of varying environmental conditions on photosynthesis. Your lab instructor MUST approve experimental design before your group can conduct this experiment.

Obtain the needed materials from the lab instructor and record your hypothesis, procedures, and data in your laboratory manual.

THINGS TO CONSIDER

Why are there multiple tubes that contain *Elodea?*

Why is there a tube that contains no *Elodea?*

Why are the tubes sealed with rubber stoppers?

Why did we use an aquatic plant rather than a terrestrial plant for our experimental system?

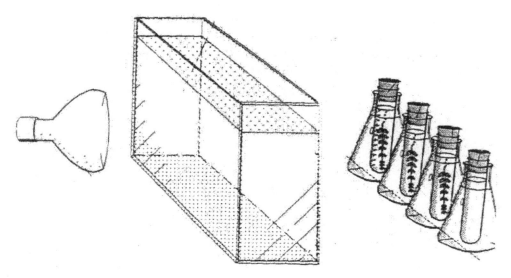

DIAGRAM 1.   *Elodea* mounted in a series of tubes with reagents to measure photosynthesis

CHAPTER 8 REVIEW QUESTIONS (5 POINTS EACH)

Name_____

1. In this activity what is happening in terms of photosynthesis when the pH level goes from acidic to basic?

2. What is happening, in terms of photosynthetic activity and the CO_2 level, when the level of the pH remains constant?

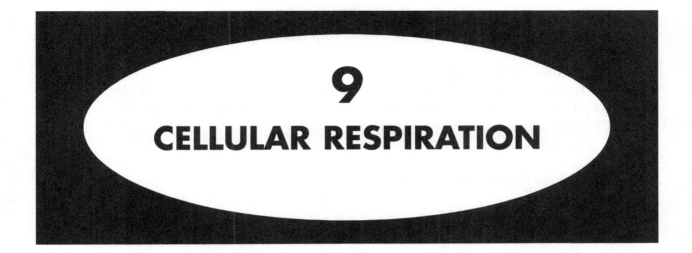

9
CELLULAR RESPIRATION

OBJECTIVES

This lab is a computer driven laboratory activity that animates the process of cellular respiration.

Students will need to go through the tutorial section of this computer program to aid in the answering of all questions concerning cellular respiration.

Be able to draw a conclusion on the test samples used in this computer animated activity on which samples had the highest rate of cellular respiration.

BACKGROUND INFORMATION

Oxidative respiration occurs in organisms in all kingdoms, strongly suggesting an ancient evolutionary origin for this process. All aerobic organisms oxidize sugars in an identical way. A simple equation for this chemical reaction is as follows:

$$C_6H_{12}O_6 + 6O_2 \xrightarrow[Enzymes]{Heat \Uparrow} 6H_2O + 6CO_2$$

The energy released by this process is stored in chemical bonds in adenosine triphosphate (ATP) for use in cellular reactions.

PROCEDURE (Computer lab)

1.   Log on to your computer using the Neo/Sci cell respiration icon (ask TA for password).

2.   Go through the **lab tutorial** section first. This will assist in answering the questions pertaining to this lab as well as help you in conducting the activity.

3.   Conduct the **Lab Investigation**
   A) Record answers to the questions at the end of the activity in your lab notebook.
   B) Transfer the graph from the lab investigation into your lab notebook.
   C) Draw a conclusion based on respiration activity and record this in your lab notebook as well.

Additional Cellular Respiration questions for your notebook;

1. What molecule is used as a power source for many cellular processes?
2. ATP is produced by three processes – What are the three processes?
3. Of these three processes where does the citric acid cycle and oxidative phosphorylation occur?
4. What does the term glycolysis mean?
5. What is the total yield of ATP for glycolysis?
6. Where are the proteins embedded that are necessary to complete the process of cellular respiration?
7. What is the starting compound in the citric acid cycle?
8. What is the removal of a carboxyl group from an organic compound?
9. What are two methods of indirectly measuring the rate of cellular respiration?
10. During cellular respiration what two gases are changing in volume?

CHAPTER 9 REVIEW QUESTIONS (10 POINTS)

Name_____

1.   What is the source of energy that drives many cellular processes?

2.   Name three processes required for the breakdown of a glucose molecule?

3.   What are the folds in the mitochondria called?

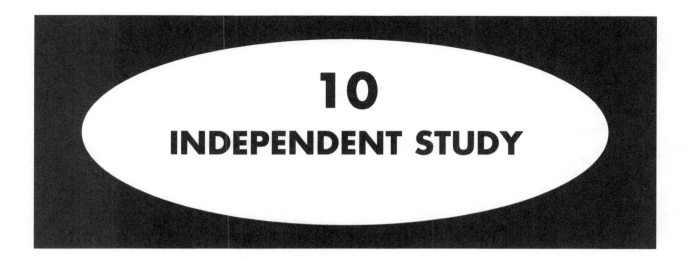

10
INDEPENDENT STUDY

BACKGROUND INFORMATION

Throughout this course, we have shown you some of the tools that can be used and suggested some additional variables for each experiment. For this lab you and your group will choose a problem, formulate a hypothesis, and design an experiment to test this hypothesis. The experiment will be carried out in one lab meeting. The following comments will provide guidelines for your experiment. You should plan to work on your experiment as a group of 3 or 4; larger groups will not be allowed because we're striving for full participation from everyone in the group. Refer to exercises you completed this term for ideas, equipment, etc.

Keep in mind that there may be restrictions on the kind of organisms available. Ask your instructor about availability. Tissues of various types may be substituted for organisms already used in lab.

Your experiments should be designed and clearly outlined one week before the scheduled class starts. Your lab instructor will approve this outline and make sure equipment is available. When you are preparing your protocol, be sure to keep in mind the following:

#1 All experiments must have controls.

#2 All experiments must have appropriate replication.

#3 The experiment must be completed in a single three hour lab (although you may prepare solutions, media, or cultures previously). See your lab instructor.

#4 The data that you collect should be quantitative, so include tables and graphs for your poster presentations of results.

#5 NO animals are to be harmed, and no human blood is to be used.

#6 Any organism used MUST BE approved by lab instructor.

#7 All experiments will be based on diffusion and osmosis (Ch.6), enzyme activity (Ch.7), or photosynthesis (Ch.8).

A PowerPoint oral presentation, and paper will be required on the Independent Study for the final class meeting.

CHAPTER 10 REVIEW QUESTIONS (5 POINTS EACH)

Name_____

1.   What activity did your group do and what changes were made from the original method?

2.   How did your results vary between the two different methods?

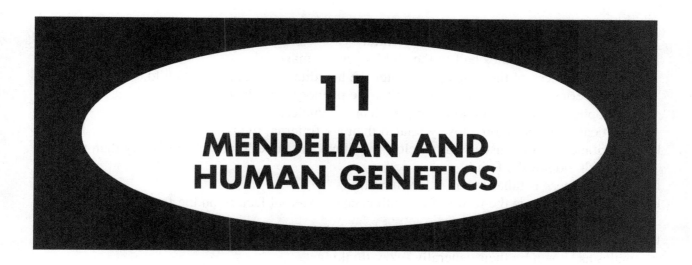

11
MENDELIAN AND HUMAN GENETICS

PURPOSE

To examine the inheritance of genetic traits in humans.

MATERIALS

Powers of observation and an open mind.

INTRODUCTION

In this exercise, you will also study inheritance of genetic traits in humans. The principles of inheritance developed by Mendel have proved applicable to all complex organisms. Although the inheritance of some human traits appears to follow simple Mendelian laws, other traits must be explained on the basis of more complicated genetic behavior. Some traits are discrete cases of "either-or" and others, such as adult body size, appear in the population over a continuous scale. Relatively few inherited traits are simple, distinct, and easily observed. Other genetic traits may be determined by **multiple alleles** or by **additive effects.** Many inherited human characteristics result from the interaction of a number of genes, but quite often the variation in the nature of only one gene produces a variation in a characteristic that gives two distinct phases of expression.

How great is your understanding of genetic principles and concepts? Have you ever heard anyone say that the male is the stronger of the two sexes, and that he controls the heredity of the child? Or have you heard anyone suggest that an expectant mother attend concerts if she wants her unborn child to become a musician? Try to answer the following true-or-false statements to determine your knowledge of genetics. The statements relate to various genetic principles, many of which are associated with common false ideas and superstitions.

1. Certain acquired characteristics, such as mechanical or mathematical skill, may be inherited.
2. Identical twins are always identical in appearance.

Written by Clifford Dill, Nebraska Wesleyan University, Lincoln NE.

3. Fraternal twins are more closely related to each other than are the other children in the family.
4. The father determines the sex of the child.
5. Each parent contributes half to the child's genetic makeup.
6. The experiences of the mother may alter the hereditary makeup of the child.
7. The experiences of the mother may alter the phenotype of the child.
8. Hemophilia is more common in males than in females.
9. Identical twins are more closely related than are fraternal twins.
10. Inheritance of traits usually more closely follows the father's side of the family than the mother's side of the family.
11. Mental illness is inherited as a dominant trait.
12. Down syndrome is the result of the influence of external factors on the fetus in the early months of development.
13. Although males are not genetically superior to females, females are less intelligent than males as shown by their generally fuzzy thinking.
14. The tendency to have twins may run in families.
15. Some traits that a person carries are not readily apparent in his or her phenotype.
16. If a person loses a limb through accident, that person is more likely to produce an offspring with a limb missing.
17. Children born to relatively old parents are usually less intelligent.
18. Children are influenced during development by the emotional attitude of the parents.
19. There are more X-linked genes than autosomally linked genes.
20. More boys are born each year than girls.

Turn to the page titled "Evaluation of Genetic Knowledge" near the end of this exercise for an explanation of the validity of each of these statements.

We will study and review these terms:
>   **Genotype**
>   **Phenotype**
>   **Homozygous**
>   **Heterozygous**
>   **Dominant**
>   **Recessive**
>   **Incomplete dominance**
>   **Multiple factors (polygenic character)**
>   **Multiple alleles**
>   **Sex-linkage**

HUMAN GENETICS

Work in pairs.

You will determine your phenotype and genotype when possible for a series of genetic traits. When you show a dominant characteristic, it is impossible to determine whether you are **homozygous,** carrying two identical genes, for this characteristic or whether you are **heterozygous,** carrying one dominant gene and one recessive gene. Hence, we use a dash (—) to represent this unknown second gene when we give the genotype. For instance, albinism is a characteristic that results when a person has two of the recessive genes (*aa*). If you are not an albino, however, you may have the genotype A*a* or AA. We express such a genotype as A—, which indicates that the nature of the second gene is unknown. Figure 1 shows six traits that are controlled by single genes.

As you test yourself for the following traits, record your results on the data sheet titled "Human Traits" near the end of this exercise. Check your phenotype, give your possible genotype, and give the total number of students in the class who show each of the characteristics. (D) indicates a dominant allele and (R) indicates a recessive allele.

PTC tasting: You will perform this test with two pieces of paper. The first is a plain piece of paper, and the second is the same as the first, except that it has the chemical phenyl-thio-carbamide (PTC) added to it. Chew the piece without the chemical and then chew the second piece. Some people can taste the chemical and others cannot. If you are uncertain as to the taste, you are a nontaster; tasters will have no doubt. The ability to taste PTC appears to be due to a single dominant gene (*T*) that may or may not be modified by other genes.

Tongue rolling: Stick your tongue out and try to roll the edges up to form a longitudinal U-shaped trough. The ability to roll is due to the musculature of the tongue, which in turn is controlled developmentally by a single gene that is dominant over that for nonrolling. How could you verify this analysis of dominance? Perhaps you could test the other members of your family for rollers and nonrollers and construct a pedigree to analyze the results.

Free ear lobes: Human ear lobes may be either free or attached to the side of the head. The gene for the free condition is dominant over that for the attached condition.

Mid-digital hair: Examine the backs of the middle digits of your fingers. Complete absence of hair on the middle digits of the fingers is a simple recessive trait in the human. Multiple alleles determine the presence or absence of mid-digital hair.

Widow's peak: In some people, the hairline drops down and forms a distinct point in the center of the forehead. This is known as a widow's peak. It results from the action of a dominant gene (*W*). Determine your phenotype by examining your front hairline for a widow's peak or a continuous hairline. (You will have to skip this tabulation if a gene for baldness has had its effect at the front part of the head).

Hitchhiker's thumb: This trait can be determined by bending the distal joint of the thumb back as far as possible. Some persons can bend it back to almost, but not quite, a 45° angle. A recessive gene (*i*) seems to determine this ability.

Bent little finger: A dominant gene (*B*) causes the last joint of the little finger to bend inward toward the fourth finger. Lay both hands flat on the table, relax the muscles, and note whether you have a bent or straight little finger.

Pigmented iris of eyes: When a person is homozygous for a certain recessive gene (*p*), no pigment is present in the front part of the eyes and a blue layer at the back of the iris shows through.

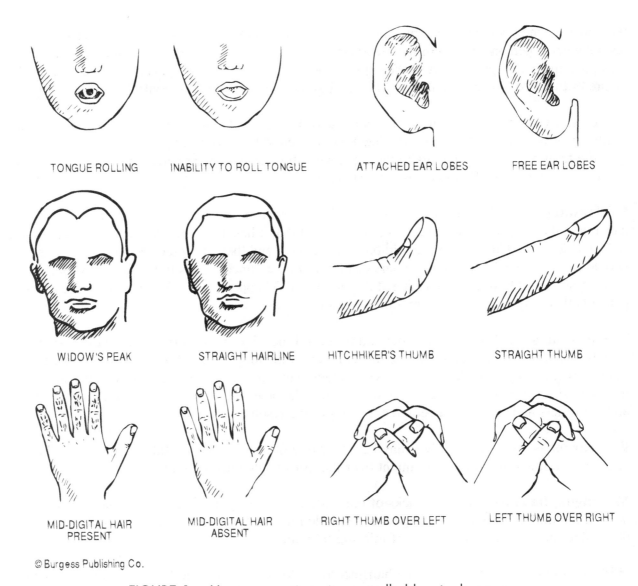

TONGUE ROLLING   INABILITY TO ROLL TONGUE   ATTACHED EAR LOBES   FREE EAR LOBES

WIDOW'S PEAK   STRAIGHT HAIRLINE   HITCHHIKER'S THUMB   STRAIGHT THUMB

MID-DIGITAL HAIR PRESENT   MID-DIGITAL HAIR ABSENT   RIGHT THUMB OVER LEFT   LEFT THUMB OVER RIGHT

© Burgess Publishing Co.

FIGURE 1. Human genetic traits controlled by single genes.

This gives blue eyes. A dominant allele of this gene (*P*) causes pigment to be deposited in the front layer of the iris, masking the blue to a varying degree. Other genes determine the exact nature and density of this pigment, so we have brown, hazel, violet, green, and other eye colors. Here we will concern ourselves only with the presence or absence of such pigment. Determine your phenotype for pigmented or unpigmented iris. (Note: Sometimes the layer at the back of the iris is gray. Count gray as unpigmented.)

Second finger shorter than fourth: Place your hands on a sheet of paper so that the fingers are at right angles to a horizontal line on the paper. Now move your hand up or down until the tip of the fourth (ring) finger barely touches one of the lines. Look at your second finger to see if it reaches the line. If it does not, your second finger is shorter than the fourth. One worker believes that this short second finger results from a gene that is influenced by the sex hormones of the individual. If so, the gene is dominant in males and recessive in females. Use the symbol Ss for the gene for short second finger and the symbol S^1 for the gene for long second finger. Tabulate the results of the class according to sex as well as second finger length.

EVALUATION OF GENETIC KNOWLEDGE

1. True. These traits are influenced by the genetic makeup of the individual and are determined by more than one pair of genes. Of course, the individual must cultivate the skill inherited.

2. False. They have the same genotype, but the phenotype may be modified by the environment such that the two twins differ slightly in some details.

3. False. By definition, fraternal twins arise from different eggs and sperm.

4. True, in humans. All normal eggs are X-bearing, and the sex is determined by whether the sperm carries an X chromosome or a Y chromosome. Certain factors apparently can modify the number or types of sperm that reach the egg.

5. True. Each contributes 23 chromosomes, but the chromosomes have qualitative differences.

6. False. See the following answer for exceptions.

7. True. Certain environmental influences, for example, thalidomide, aminopterin, busulfan, and rubella, may alter the phenotype if the embryo or fetus is susceptible at the time of treatment. The genotype of a fetus may be altered by therapeutic radiation and other sources of ionizing radiation.

8. True. X-linked genes in humans are expressed more frequently in males if the gene is recessive.

9. True. See 2 above.

10. False. See 5 above.

11. False. Some evidence suggests that certain behavior patterns such as schizophrenia are inherited, but most likely as a recessive trait. Some forms of schizophrenia are environmentally caused. Other forms of mental illness are being studied to determine if they have a genetic component.

12. False. Down syndrome results from an individual having an extra chromosome 21. Chromosome number is determined at the time of fertilization rather than by external influence during subsequent development.

13. False.

14. True. Evidence suggests that fraternal twins occur in certain families, and this twinning follows the maternal side of the family. Why? Likewise, tentative evidence suggests that in a few families identical twins are familial.

15. True. Recessive traits are not expressed when masked by a dominant allele, and even some dominant traits may not be expressed under certain conditions during development.

16. False. In one experiment, the tails of mice were cut off in each generation, but the next progeny continued to be born with tails.

17. False. There seems to be indication that the firstborn individual in a family is a higher achiever, but this is not necessarily related to the intelligence. The intelligence and achievement of firstborn individuals might be related to factors such as the uterine environment or peculiarities of the social situation. Most Down syndrome children are born to mothers over age 35.

18. False. However, prolonged stress and the accompanying physiological imbalances might affect development; the effects of low-level, long-term stress are unknown.

19. False. Nonetheless, X-linked recessive genes and dominant genes occurring on any chromosome are more easily recognized in most species.

20. True. The ratio of females to males at birth in most populations varies, but in one population it has been 1.00 females: 1.05 males for several decades.

HUMAN TRAITS

	Check your phenotype	Give your genotype	Number of each in the class
PTC taster (D)	_____	_____	_____
Nontaster of PTC (R)	_____	_____	_____
Can roll tongue (D)	_____	_____	_____
Cannot roll tongue (R)	_____	_____	_____
Attached ear lobes (R)	_____	_____	_____
Free ear lobes (D)	_____	_____	_____
No mid-digital hair (R)	_____	_____	_____
Mid-digital hair (D)	_____	_____	_____
Widow's peak (D)	_____	_____	_____
No widow's peak (R)	_____	_____	_____
Hitchhiker's thumb (R)	_____	_____	_____
No hitchhiker's thumb (D)	_____	_____	_____
Bent little finger (D)	_____	_____	_____
Straight little finger (R)	_____	_____	_____
Pigmented iris (D)	_____	_____	_____
No pigmented iris (R)	_____	_____	_____
Second finger shorter than the fourth	♂ _____	_____	_____
	♀ _____	_____	_____

VARIATION IN A HUMAN POPULATION

PURPOSE

Demonstrate the concept of variability in a population.

MATERIALS

Millimeter ruler

INTRODUCTION

A **population** of organisms is a group of individuals of the same species occupying a given area at a given time. For example, you and your colleagues in the laboratory at the moment are a population; you are all *Homo sapiens*. Your population consists of the humans in biology class right now.

Most scientists agree that variability within a species is important to its survival.

PART A—COLLECTING THE DATA, MALE HAND SPANS

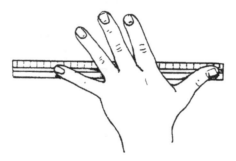

FIGURE 1. Measuring hand span.

1. MEASURE THE SPAN OF YOUR LEFT HAND, as shown in Figure 1. Your wrist should touch the table top. Measure the distance from the tip of your little finger to the tip of your thumb, to the nearest centimeter. If the measure is to an even 5 mm, round up to the next centimeter.

   What is the measurement of your hand span?

Written by Burgess Editors with Ed Perry, James H. Faulkner State Community College, Bay Minette, AL

2. CONTRIBUTE YOUR DATA TO THE TOTALS ON THE BOARD. Your instructor will have three groups of data: one for males, one for females, and one for both sexes. Each group will contain a list of measurements, and you will put a mark for yours in the proper place.

3. FILL IN TABLE 1 WITH THE INFORMATION ON THE BOARD.

   Table 1. Numbers of males with the same measurements. N = number of individuals.

cm	N	cm	N	cm	N
16	____	21	____	26	____
17	____	22	____	27	____
18	____	23	____	28	____
19	____	24	____	29	____
20	____	25	____	30	____

4. CONSTRUCT A BAR GRAPH SHOWING THESE TOTALS. Place the measurements along the bottom. Begin with 16 at the left, continue to 30 to the right. Number the vertical spaces along the left side, 0 at the bottom to 12 at top.

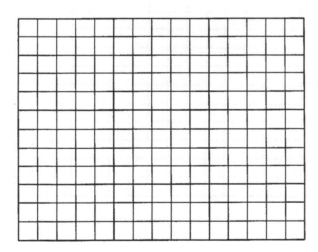

Male hand spans

PART B—COLLECTING THE DATA, FEMALE HAND SPANS

1. FILL IN TABLE 2 WITH THE INFORMATION FROM THE BOARD FOR FEMALES

   Table 2. Numbers of females with the same measurements. N = number of individuals.

cm	N	cm	N	cm	N
16	___	21	___	26	___
17	___	22	___	27	___
18	___	23	___	28	___
19	___	24	___	29	___
20	___	25	___	30	___

2. CONSTRUCT A BAR GRAPH SHOWING THESE TOTALS. Place the measurements along the bottom. Begin with 16 at the left, continue to 30 to the right. Number the vertical spaces along the left side, 0 at the bottom to 12 at top.

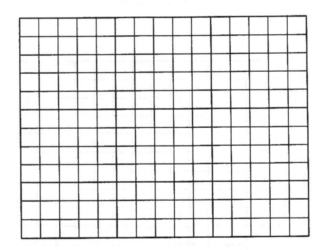

Female hand spans

PART C—ANALYZING THE DATA

1. COMBINE THE TOTALS FOR MALES AND FEMALES AND ENTER THE NUMBERS IN TABLE 3.

   Table 3. Numbers of students with the same measurements. N = number of individuals.

cm	N	cm	N	cm	N
16	____	21	____	26	____
17	____	22	____	27	____
18	____	23	____	28	____
19	____	24	____	29	____
20	____	25	____	30	____

2. CONSTRUCT A BAR GRAPH SHOWING THESE TOTALS.

   Place the measurements along the bottom. Begin with 16 at the left, continue to 30 to the right. Number the vertical spaces along the left side, 0 at the bottom to 12 at top.

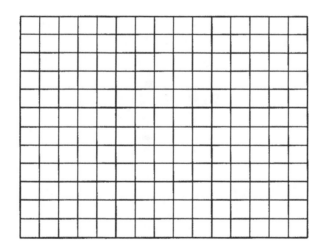

Student hand spans, both sexes

Are the hand spans of all the males in your class the same?

Which male hand span occurs the most often?

What is the range of male hand spans measured in your class?

Are the hand spans of all the females in your class the same?

Which female hand span occurs the most often?

What is the range of female hand spans measured in your class?

Which hand span occurs most often among the students in your class?

What is the range of hand spans measured in your class?

What is meant by the term "variation"?

CHAPTER 11 REVIEW QUESTIONS (2 POINTS EACH)

Name_____

1.   Are identical twins always the same in appearance?

2.   Is Down syndrome the result of an external factor on the fetus during early development?

3.   Can what a mother experiences while she is pregnant alter the phenotype of her child?

4.   Some traits that a person carries are not readily apparent in his or her phenotype.

5.   What was the range of hand spans measured in your class?

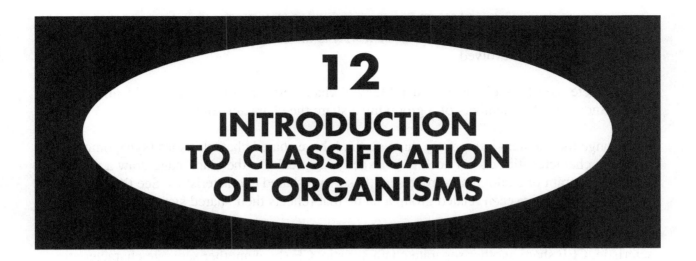

OBJECTIVE

To become familiar with how evolutionary biologists use morphological data to describe the evolutionary history and relationships of a group of organisms.

BACKGROUND INFORMATION

This laboratory exercise is a simplified approach of a procedure used by many modern systematic biologists for classifying organisms. The purpose is to reconstruct the evolution of a mythical group of organisms. This is not an easy task when all you have is the extant (living today) species and their morphology to use. To make this approach scientific it must be as objective as possible. Cladistical analysis is a semi-objective tool used to organize a number of organisms in groups based on their morphological traits.

SOME TERMS

Autapomorphy: a characteristic that makes an organism unique.
Dendrogram: a branching diagram to show relationships between objects.
Outgroup: A primitive organism used as a reference point. The rest of the organisms in the group have evolved from this primitive organism or from a group that evolved from it.
Synapomorphy: a unique morphological characteristic shared by a group of organisms.

PROCEDURE

Each group will have a set of pictures of the mythological organisms in the order Rhinogradentia (the rhinogrades or snouters). Carefully study the pictures of the organisms. Pay careful attention to the modifications of the rhinarium (nose) and the appendages (arms, legs, and wings). You will see that the morphological characteristics are a combination of characteristics shared by different snouters (synapomorphies), and characteristics that make each species of snouter unique (autapomorphies). The snouters are labeled A–K. Treat each as a different species. The organism, *Archirrhinos haeckelii* (A) is the most primitive snouter (outgroup) from which the others have evolved.

1) Complete the Morphological Data Table with characteristics your group has identified on the Snouters. All members of a group must share the characteristic(s)

2) Arrange the snouters into groups that you think have shared characteristics (synapomorphies). These characteristics do not need to be exactly identical. On the blank page draw a nested-hoop diagram or cladogram to represent those with shared characteristics. See the example below. Try to give each related group a name that reflects their shared synapomorphy.

EXAMPLE: BCDEF all share a characteristic (synapomorphy), BD share another separate characteristic, CEF share another separate characteristic, CE share another separate characteristic.

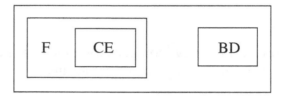

3) Draw an evolutionary tree (dendrogram) that attempts to show the branch points in the evolution of the snouters. Below is an example of such a dendrogram.

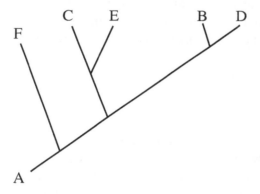

4) Copy your cladogram and dendrogram on the acetate sheet so that it may be projected on the screen. It will be interesting to see how the work of your group compares with that of other groups.

This laboratory exercise is based on the book entitled "The Snouters, Form and Life of the Rhinogrades." Translated by Leigh Chadwick, from the original German work entitled "Bau und Leben der Rhinogradentia," written by Harold Strumke. It is a wonderful biological tale about a mythical group of animals. It discusses their morphology, development, physiology, behavior, and evolution.

CHAPTER 12 REVIEW QUESTIONS (2 POINTS EACH)

Name_____

1. These mythical animals are all placed in the Order Rhinogradentia. What is the next most inclusive taxonomic unit (has more different kinds of species)?

2. What is the next less inclusive taxonomic unit (has fewer different kinds of species)?

3. What taxonomic unit contains a single kind of organism?

4. What common ancestor do you share with your cousins?

5. In the dendrogram on page 12–82 what is the relationship of organism C to organisms A and B?

13

CLASS RESEARCH PROJECT: HABITAT DESCRIPTION

OBJECTIVE

Students will gain a broad understanding of the area in which they live and the organisms they share with it.

BACKGROUND INFORMATION

You and your group will compare the biological diversity of 2 habitat types on the Tech campus or nearby areas. This information will be collected and reported by each group to the class at the end of the quarter (last lab meeting). This data shall include a hypothesis that could account for the differences you observed with these habitats.

One of the habitats will be an area classified under the category of "open area." "Open areas" will include grass/weedy/lawn-like areas that LACK trees. The second area will be a "woodland" area; an area where there is a canopy (covering) of trees.

The areas you choose to sample will be up to you; however, the areas that you choose must be large enough for five sample plots of 1 square meter.

Your group will use a sampling device that is made of a 4 meter long string that when stretched into a square, will enclose a 1 square meter area. Some other important tools to be used for sampling will be your eyes, hands and brains. To conduct your sampling exercise you will need only these tools along with some containers for the organisms you collect and your notebook for writing down the observations you will need to make.

THE RULES FOR STUDY

No trespassing; get permission before you go on any property. Hideaway Park is a good place to have your woodland set of plots. If your group has access to an area other than the Tech campus, that's fine (you must get permission to use this area). The object of this study is to see as much diversity as possible. Do not harm anything! We will sample leaves and flowers from plants. We will not sample any higher animals (snakes, squirrels, etc.) we find on our plots. This study will be limited to the Kingdom Plantae.

SCHEDULE

In your group discuss the possible habitats that you will study. Choose a site on the Louisiana Tech Campus where your activities will not cause any disturbance. This decision needs to be made as soon as possible. Group needs to meet at the sites and make observations and collect specimens.

During the following weeks of class your group will meet to identify organisms collected and analyze data.
The final project is to be turned in during lab when your group conducts their oral presentation (the 8th lab meeting). Your entire group will be required to participate in the oral presentation of this project. All presentations will be during the 8th lab meeting of the quarter and each group member will be graded on presentation.

The project will consist of:

–A statistical analysis of species richness using JMPin statistical software
–Comparison of Habitat Diversity work sheet (one per group)
–Oral presentation (by entire group)

PROCEDURE

Each group will have the following materials to work with:

1 meter square plot markers
Envelopes for collected organisms

Group members will describe each habitat and make collections of the organisms found within the habitat and identify (classify) each organism collected. You will be part of team and will be expected to contribute to the group effort.

Use the form **COMPARISON OF HABITAT DIVERSITY**

Instructions for the form:

This is what will be used to grade you and your group on this project.
Hand in one per group with all group members names included.

Give the precise location of the habitat (corner of 18th street and Wabash, front yard of residence, landscaped lawn area, etc.)

Describe the habitat:

    Topography (vacant lot, landscaped, dense woods, hilly, flat, low area that floods, high area etc.)
    Soil Type (sandy, clay, rocky, etc.)
    Sun Exposure (partly, full sun, shade)
    Moisture (wet, dry)

List all organisms found in the habitat area. Indicate the relative abundance of each organism listed as: rare, occasional, common, or abundant. Absolute identification is not necessary; your observations over the next few weeks in lab and class will be helpful in the identification of some of your organisms to the following levels of classification.

Domain
    Kingdom
           Phylum (Division)
                Class
                    Order

Determining the absolute identity of your organisms is not the purpose of this project. Your job is to identify the diversity present in your plots. Ideally you will be able to identify each organism at the Order or Class level. You may find that some of the organisms can only be identified as Monocotoledenae 1 or Monocotoledenae 2, etc.

For plants, collect a few leaves, flowers or seed pods as this will help when trying to identify the plant. You may wish to take photographs of some of your organisms.

We have software located in the lab that can be used to help identify organisms (see your lab instructor).

Calculate species richness for each of your woodland plots.

    Total # species plot 1
    Total # species plot 2
    Total # species plot 3
    Total # species plot 4
    <u>Total # species plot 5</u>
    Sum of all plots /5 = Average species richness for woodland

Repeat the above for your open area samples.

Draw a map of the habitat indicating the major biological and non-biological features. On the map indicate the location of the five 1-meter-square sampling plots.

BIOLOGY 133 LABORATORY—COMPARISON OF HABITAT DIVERSITY

Group Number _____   First Meeting Date _____

Group Members

_____   _____

_____   _____

_____   _____

_____

1. State your group hypothesis concerning the diversity you expect to find in an open vs. a wooded habitat.

2. Describe the precise location of the habitats your group has chosen to study.
   A. Open Habitat

   B. Wooded Habitat

3. Describe the sampling method used to choose and assess the plots you will study.

4. Describe the Environmental Condition in the habitats
   A. Open Habitat
      a. Soil

      b. Sun exposure

      c. Moisture

      d. Topography

   B. Wooded Habitat
      a. Soil

      b. Sun exposure

      c. Moisture

      d. Topography

5. List the Fungi and Plants in the Habitat samples and the total number of each in the samples.

   A. Open Habitat

   B. Wooded Habitat

6. Attach a sheet with the results of your statistical analysis.

7. Give a statement of your conclusions from the data concerning the relative diversity of the two habitats studied.

8. How does this statement relate to your hypothesis?

CHAPTER 13 REVIEW QUESTIONS (2 POINTS EACH)

Name_____

1.   What are the two types of habitats your group will study?

2.   What type of organisms will be sampled for this study?

3.   What is the size of each sample plot?

4.   What is a general description of a "woodland" area?

5.   How many total plots will be sampled in this habitat study?

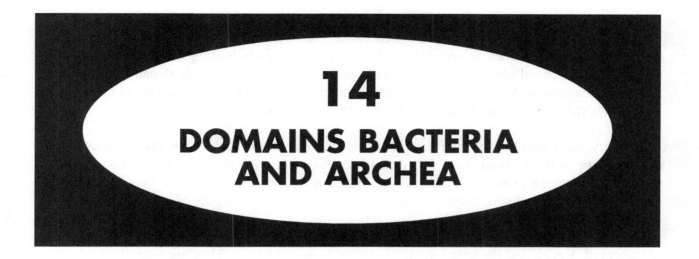

14
DOMAINS BACTERIA
AND ARCHEA

OBJECTIVES

Introduce students to representative organisms of Domains Bacteria and Archea, and the key features that set them apart from the Domain Eukaria.

BACKGROUND INFORMATION

The Archea and Bacteria both include organisms commonly called " bacteria" or "Prokaryotes." These include approximately 3000 described species (this is 6-10% of the total number of species believed to exist) of relatively simple, very small, unicellular organisms that resemble the first life to have originated on planet Earth.

The earliest forms of these organisms date to 3.6 to 3.8 billion years ago based on the fossil record. The cells of all Prokaryotes have a cell wall and a plasma membrane that encloses the cytoplasmic contents including DNA, ribosomes, and a myriad of enzymes that function in chemical reactions. However, Prokaryotes (except a few cyanobacteria) lack nuclei and membrane bounded organelles. Their DNA consists of a circular strand that is not associated with histone proteins. They replicate by means of fission; they do not undergo mitosis or meiosis. Prokaryotes are marvels of miniaturization; in fact, they are about the size of Eukaryotic organelles such as mitochondria and chloroplasts (both now believed to have once been free living members of the Bacteria). The DNA of Prokaryotes is streamlined with very few non-coding sequences; it is transcribed and translated very efficiently into proteins. Prokaryotes can transport nutrients across the plasma membrane rapidly and are often able to out-compete Eukaryotes for scarce nutrients. Because they grow and divide very quickly, Prokaryotes can exploit energy sources before Eukaryotes can respond. Because they are encased in a rigid cell wall, Prokaryotes obtain their nutrients in soluble form. They therefore cannot attack large masses of food as do the fungi and most animals, but must absorb nutrients directly from the environment after secreting enzymes externally.

Despite their similarities, Archea and the Bacteria differ in some major features and apparently represent two major, early lineages of life on earth. The Archea include organisms that live in extreme environments such as very salty water, very hot to nearly boiling water, or water rich in sulfur or hydrogen sulfide such as that of deep sea vents. They lack peptidoglycans in their cell walls. Archea possess RNA polymerase and ribosomal RNA that is more similar to those of Eukaryotes (like you and me) than to members of the Bacteria.

Conversely, most members of the Bacteria have peptidoglycans in their cell walls and possess a different type of RNA polymerase. The group Bacteria is currently divided into several subgroups that will not concern us here. Members of the Bacteria are found in nearly every ecological niche on the planet including soil, water, the surface of animals and plants, guts of animals, plus many of the niches occupied by the Archea.

Members of Archea and Bacteria are rather simple in general form. They are unicellular, the cells being of three standard shapes—**cocci** (spherical), **bacilli** (rod shaped), and **spirilloid** (spiral). Several species are filamentous (the cells line up end to end to form a long chain). Some species are **colonial,** (aggregated into small groups) such as the colonial cyanobacteria (Gleocapsa). Some are mobile by means of **flagella;** several groups produce resistant resting structures called **spores.**

The species of the Archea and Bacteria exhibit either of two major types of metabolic pathways: **autotrophic** and **heterotrophic.** Heterotrophic species are those that require pre-existing high-energy organic compounds for survival. There are two types of heterotrophic bacteria, **saprotrophs** (saprobes) and **biotrophs.** Saprotrophs are those that live on dead organic matter and are important decomposers in the food chain. The biotrophic bacteria require a living host and may be **mutualists** (beneficial to their host) or **parasites** (detrimental to their hosts). Parasitic species include bacterial pathogens that cause many serious diseases including plant blights and human diseases such as cholera, tetanus, bacterial pneumonia, tuberculosis, bacterial dysentery, the venereal diseases gonorrhea and syphilis, and the dental plaque on your funky nasty teeth.

Autotrophic bacteria are those that are capable of manufacturing their own organic compounds from carbon dioxide in the atmosphere. These include **chemoautotrophs,** which manufacture high-energy organic compounds by using non-organic chemical reactions, and **photoautotrophs** (or photosynthetic bacteria), which manufacture high-energy organic compounds by using sunlight. Included in these are the **cyanobacteria** (often called blue-green bacteria or blue-green algae). Photoautotrophs convert solar energy into chemical energy stored in glucose with the use of green pigments. In the process they break water molecules into hydrogen and oxygen: oxygen is released in the process. This is the same type of photosynthesis found in the Protista (algae), as well as in plants.

Cyanobacteria (blue-green algae) are responsible for the largest single pollution event ever to happen here on planet Earth. Some 2.6 billion years ago the oxygen holocaust began. Photosynthetic bacteria, using sunlight to crack water molecules and fix carbon dioxide, gave off the hellishly toxic O_2 as a byproduct, causing the extinction of most of the Prokaryotes ever seen on planet earth. Many of the blue-green algae have specialized cells that fix atmospheric nitrogen by converting the N_2 gas into ammonia, an essential mineral nutrient for the production of amino acids.

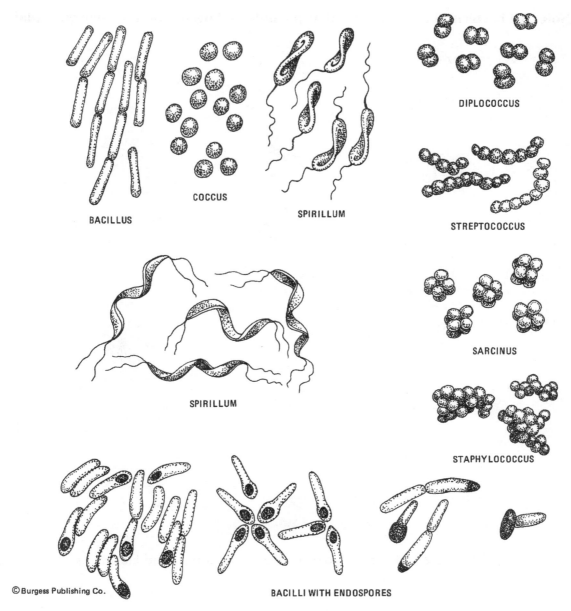

FIGURE 1.   Bacterial Morphology (Typical)

BACILLUS

COCCUS

SPIRILLUM

DIPLOCOCCUS

STREPTOCOCCUS

SPIRILLUM

SARCINUS

STAPHYLOCOCCUS

© Burgess Publishing Co.

BACILLI WITH ENDOSPORES

EXERCISE 1 OBSERVE BACTERIAL COLONIES

Observe plates and note any bacterial colonies that grow on them. Bacterial colonies generally appear as white or colored, not cottony, gelatinous discs or splotches. Draw and describe the colonies noting the color, texture (smooth or rough), and surface appearance (glossy or dull).

Note: All bacteria should be treated as possible pathogens! Do not open your plates!

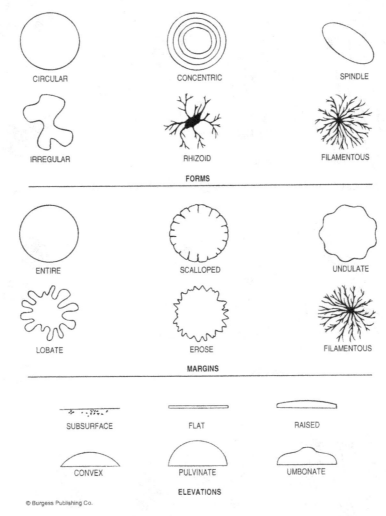

FIGURE 2. Bacterial Colonies, Forms, Margins, and Elevations

EXERCISE 2 BACTERIAL CELL MORPHOLOGY

Demonstration slides will be set out at stations in the lab. Observe the three major bacterial forms: rod, spherical, and spiral. See your instructor for proper procedures for using the 100X oil immersion objectives on a microscope. Many of the heterotrophic Prokaryotes are grouped into **gram positive** and **gram negative** staining species. When bacterial cells are stained by a process called a Gram stain, gram positive (+) bacteria appear blue and gram negative (–) bacteria appear pink. The color difference between the plus and minus species is based on the components and structure of their cell walls. Draw and label three major bacterial cell morphologies and the + or – gram stained bacteria as well. Be sure to include the magnification of your drawings.

EXERCISE 3 CYANOBACTERIA

Observe the prepared slides of Cyanobacteria and fresh material if available. Note the cell size, the blue-green color, and the lack of large organelles and nuclei. Some species will form specialized cells called Heterocysts, which can fix nitrogen. Examine the following Cyanobacteria available on the prepared slides: *Nostoc, Oscillatoria, Gleocapsa.* Describe and draw these in your notebook.

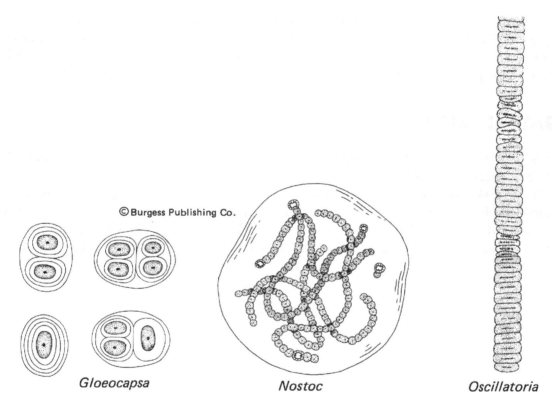

© Burgess Publishing Co.

Gloeocapsa   *Nostoc*   *Oscillatoria*

FIGURE 3.   Common Cyanobacteria

EXERCISE 4 SYMBIOSIS AND ECONOMICALLY IMPORTANT BACTERIA

A container of clover plants will be available for your group to use to observe root nodules. Each group should obtain one container and gently remove the plants from the soil. Soil needs to be removed from roots by using a gentle flow of water. Once soil has been removed from roots, place the plant under a dissecting microscope to view the nodules. Remove nodules from the root using a scalpel and place on a slide in a small drop of water. Next place a cover glass over the top of nodule and gently press down on cover glass using the small dowel rod so that the nodule is ruptured. Next observe the bacterial cells that are expelled from the nodule.

Observe the root nodules of a legume (member of the pea/beans family). Prepared slides may be available of the bacteria living symbiotically in the roots of the plant. Describe this association.

EXERCISE 5 HAY INFUSION SET UP

Each group needs one Mason jar. In the Mason jar place a small amount of dried hay (5–20 pieces) then fill the jar ¾ full with pond water. Jars should be labeled and left open and placed in an out-of-the-way location. Your hay infusion will be used during next week's lab for observation of organism. Be sure to wash your hands after setting up your hay infusion jar.

LITERATURE CITED

Kumar, S. and Rzhetsky. 1996. Evolutionary relationships of eukaryotic kingdoms. Journal of Molecular Evolution 42:183–193

Sogin, M.L. 1994. The origin of eukaryotes and evolution into major kingdoms. In: Bengtson, S. (ed). Nobel Symposium, No 84. Early life on Earth; 84th Nobel symposium Karlskoga, Sweden, May 16, 1992. 630 P. Columbia University Press NY, NY. USA. p182–192

Pace, N. 1997. A molecular view of microbial diversity in the biosphere. Science 276:735

CHAPTER 14 REVIEW QUESTIONS (5 POINTS EACH)

Name_____

1.   Describe the structure and function of the nodules on the roots of clover.

2.   Describe the structure and movement of *Oscillatoria*.

15
DOMAIN EUKARYA, KINGDOMS PROTISTA AND FUNGI

OBJECTIVE

Introduce students to a variety of examples from these diverse groups of organisms and the key features that set them apart from the Prokaryotes and the Kingdoms Animalia and Plantae.

BACKGROUND INFORMATION

INTRODUCTION TO THE EUKARYOTES, KINGDOM "PROTISTA"

The "Protista" (in quotes because this is a paraphyletic assemblage of organism) is a large diverse group of mostly unicellular organisms that constitute a number of the first lineages of Eukaryotes to have evolved from ancestral Archea and Bacteria. The "Protista" differ from prokaryotes by having linear DNA associated with histone proteins and membrane-bounded organelles. Many of the membrane-bounded organelles arose through the process of **endosymbiosis** in which an ancient prokaryote was engulfed but not consumed by an ancient Eukaryotic cell. **Mitochondria, chloroplasts,** and **centrioles/flagella** have arisen this way. The evidence for endosymbiosis is numerous and includes that chloroplasts and mitochondria 1) contain single stranded circular DNA, 2) contain small sized 70s ribosomes, and 3) replicate by binary fission independent of the nucleus. In time, bacteria that had been engulfed by ancient prokaryotes lost their independence and became dependent upon the nuclear genome of the host cell for synthesis of some functional compounds. It is now believed that several separate events gave rise to chloroplasts in the major lineages of Eucaryotes.

The **unicellular heterotrophic** members of the "Protista" occupy a wide variety of habitats, can be aerobic or anaerobic, and can participate in parasitic, mutualistic, or commensal relationships with members of other Kingdoms. Included in this group are the heterotrophic amoebae and slime molds.

Heterotrophic groups:
Rhizopodia (amoebae)
Actinopodia (radiolarians, and others)
Formanifera (shell forming heterotrophs primarily in marine ecosystems)
Ampicomplexa (sporozoans such as *Plasmodium,* the cause of Malaria)
Zomastigophera (*Trypanosoma* and other flagellated heterotrophs)
Acrasiomycota (cellular slime molds)

Demonstrations slides will be provided. Observe the major forms from the groups available in lab. Observe the various **adaptations** these single celled organisms have for their particular way of life.

Biologists still do not understand fully the evolutionary relationships of groups represented in the artificial assemblage of organisms labeled "Protista." The "Protista" show tremendous diversity of life forms and life cycle types; they are usually defined by what they lack, rather than what they have. Recent work has attempted to classify these organisms into a number of monophyletic groups, but the interrelationships of these groups is still uncertain. For convenience we will continue to treat these diverse lineages as a single group called "Protista" until more complete knowledge of their evolutionary relationships is obtained.

In this lab we will focus on the diversity of the protista and fungi by observing nutrition and locomotion in these organisms.

Algae are generally defined as single- to multi-cellular photosynthetic autotrophs found primarily in aquatic environments, comprising about 25,000 species. These organisms are divided into several groups based on the photosynthetic pigments they possess, energy storage compounds and cell wall components. In the past, algae have been classified as plants, recently biologists have begun to realize that each group is in fact a separate evolutionary lineage. In addition, some of these groups are closely related to and should include organisms previously classified as fungi, the most notable example being the Oomycetes (one of many groups commonly called water molds).

The life cycle types of members of the algae are varied and complex. We still do not know fully how all these features arose during evolutionary history. Individual taxa in each of the lineages may be unicellular, colonial, filamentous, or may consist of a **thalus** - a multi cellular "body" that is not differentiated into roots, stems, and leaves. A thallus may be simple or quite complex consisting of a **holdfast** with root-like extensions, a stem-like **stipe,** and leaf-like **blades.**

This group is diverse containing mostly photoautotrophs and a few heterotrophic parasites. One of the groups of algae is the **Heterokonts.** The most basal lineage of the Heterokonts is the **Oomycetes,** once classified with the fungi because of their similarity of vegetative cells and absorptive nutrition. However, both cellular features and molecular data have confirmed that their affinities are actually with the Heterokonts. All flagellated members of this group have 2 morphologically distinct flagella; one is a simple whiplash and the other has hair-like appendages called **tinsel.** Some members of the Oomycota are economically important because they cause serious plant diseases such as powdery mildew and potato blight.

The other major lineages of Heterokontes are the **chromobionta;** they are all photosynthetic autotrophs. Apomorphies that unite them are the occurrence of photosynthesis, the presence of **chlorophyll c** in addition to **chlorophyll a** and the presence of karotinoids such as ß-carotene that cause these organisms to have a characteristic yellow green gold or brownish coloration. This group consists of the **Pheophyta** (brown algae), **Xanthophyta** (yellow brown algae), **Chrysophyta** (golden algae), and the **Baciliarophyta** (diatoms). Many of these organisms are significant as they contribute up to 50% of the primary productivity in marine ecosystems.

The **Rhodobionta** are commonly known as the red algae. Red algae are a distinctive group united by several apomorphies including the loss of flagellated cells. Red algae have a unique type of **chlorophyll d** in addition to chlorophyll a. Red algae also have a unique, water soluble photosynthetic pigment called **phycobillians,** which may be red or blue in color. Some cyanobacteria have the same photosynthetic pigments as the red algae; evidence that an ancestral endosymbiosis event gave rise to this eukaryote.

Red algae may be unicellular, but most are multi cellular and macroscopic. Some red algae secrete outer skeletons of calcium carbonate; these are called the coralline red algae. These photosynthetic organisms are important reef builders in some parts of the world. Red algae have quite complex life histories with three phases: two diploid generations that produce non-motile spores and one generation that produces **non-motile** gametes.

The **Chlorobionta** is a monophyletic group that traditionally includes the green algae plus land plants (embryophytes). The green algae alone are a paraphyletic group, usually included in the "Protista". We will cover this group next week when we begin the study of the Kingdom Plantae.

FUNGI

Another major group of Eukaryotes of great diversity and economic importance is the Fungi. The Fungi contain more than 100,000 named species. The Fungi were long ago classified as plants because they lack mobility, have rigid cell walls, and produce spores. Recent work has shown that the true Kingdom Fungi represents a monophyletic group that is the sister group to the Animal Kingdom. There are four major groups of fungi: the **Chytridiomycota** (water molds), **Zygomycota** (bread molds), **Ascomycota** (sack fungi), and the **Basidiomycota** (club fungi). Fungi and animals share multiple features in common including energy storage compounds, a single posterior flagellum (when present), and a derived type of mitochondrial genetic code.

The fungi are a monophyletic assemblage of organisms that are characterized as multi-cellular non-photosynthetic heterotrophic organisms. Cell walls are made largely of chitin, a polymer of ß 1-4 glucose. Fungi usually have **hyphae** consisting of elongate tubular cells linked together to form the body of the organism, the **mycelium.** Fungi feed by externally secreting enzymes and absorbing the food products that are broken down.

Fungi may occupy a variety of ecological niches. Many are **saprotrophic** and decompose dead organic matter and are very important components of the food chain. For example, practically all the biomass of a typical fungus is found within organic rich soils or rotten logs. Only when sexual reproduction occurs do the fungi produce a reproductive structure—either a mushroom, cup or other spore bearing structure. Other fungi are **biotrophic** (require their carbon from a living host) and many are **parasitic.** Parasitic fungi cause very important plant diseases such as rusts and smuts as well as several diseases of humans such as ringworm, athlete's foot, and others.

Finally some fungi are **mutualistic,** living in intimate contact with the host in a relationship in which both fungus and host benefit. The most important mutualistic fungi are those that are found in mycorrhizae. The term mycorrhizae refers to a relationship between a fungus and the roots of virtually all land plants. In this symbiosis, the fungus obtains high-energy organic compounds from the roots of the host plant. In return the fungi greatly increases the plant's absorptive efficiency for mineral nutrients (especially phosphorous and water). Mycorrhizae are not uncommon. In fact, virtually all plants on land form mycorrhizal associations without which they'd not survive! As evidence that mycorrhizae are the rule and not the exception, recent fossil discoveries from the Rhiney chert sedimentary rocks that are over 460 million years old contain samples of the Glomales (the fungi that form mycorrhizae). When the very first land plants arose and crawled out of the primordial soup, the fungi were most likely already attached to their "root" systems. It is a great advantage for the photosynthetic organisms to live symbiotically with an organism already specialized for an absorptive nutrition. Primitive "roots" of 400 million-year-old fossilized Agalophyton (one of the first land plants) show mycorrhiza-like structures identical to ones found in land plants today.

Another example of a mutualistic symbiosis is the association between various fungi and one or more photosynthetic algae forming a composite organism known as a **lichen.** Lichens are common and found in virtually every ecosystem on earth. They are some of the first organisms found during primary succession and can be found growing on bare rock! The fungus in the partnership determines the shape, and the algae determines the color. Sometimes the partnership will include a cyanobacteria, allowing the lichen to fix nitrogen. Vast herds of Caribou (reindeer) feed on lichens in the arctic tundra for most of the winter when other food is absent. Lichens are extremely tough in the wild but suffer badly from human impact, especially air pollution. If you see lots of lichens on trees in your neighborhood, be glad. The presence of lichens means the air is pretty clean!

EXERCISE 1 HETEROTROPHIC "PROTISTA" THE CILIATES

Paramecium and termite commensal organisms. Demonstration slides and live organisms will be available. Observe the major forms from the cilliated/flagelated groups available in lab. Observe the various adaptations these organisms have for their particular way of life. The symbiotic ciliates that live in the gut of the termite are the organisms that actually eat your house; the termites just chew it up for them!

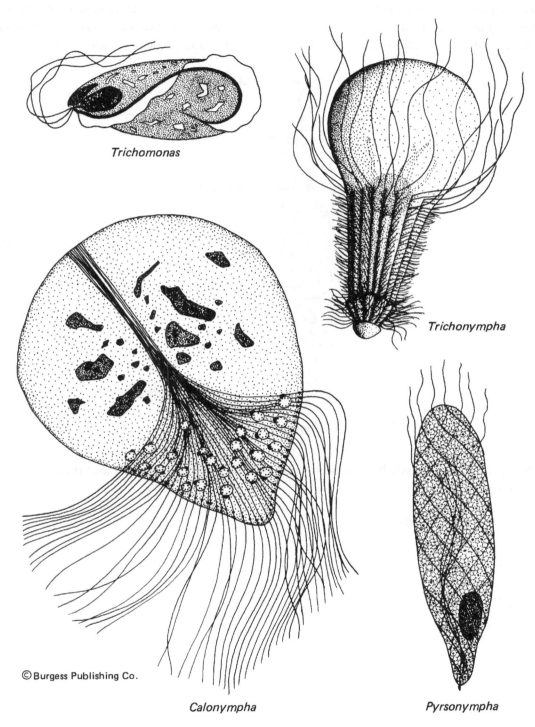

Trichomonas

Trichonympha

© Burgess Publishing Co.

Calonympha

Pyrsonympha

Common Ciliated Microorganisms

EXERCISE 2 PHOTOSYNTHETIC "PROTISTA"

Representatives of the Protista will be available for observation. Note the diverse form and function of these organisms. Euglena are unique among the flagellated Protista. Some are photosynthetic, some are predatory, and some do both! Note the live and preserved examples in lab today.

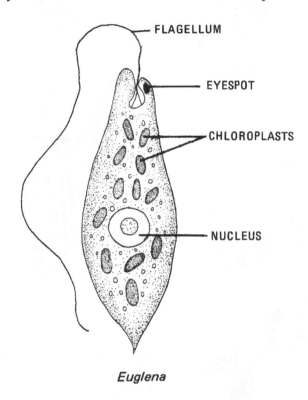

Euglena

Amoeba is a protist that moves by extending parts of the cell (pseudopod) and then flowing the rest of the cytoplasm into it.

EXERCISE 3 FUNGI

Observe the fresh and preserved slides/samples of the various members of the Kingdom Fungi.
NOTE THE LIFE CYCLES OF THESE DIVERSE HETEROTROPHIC ORGANISMS.

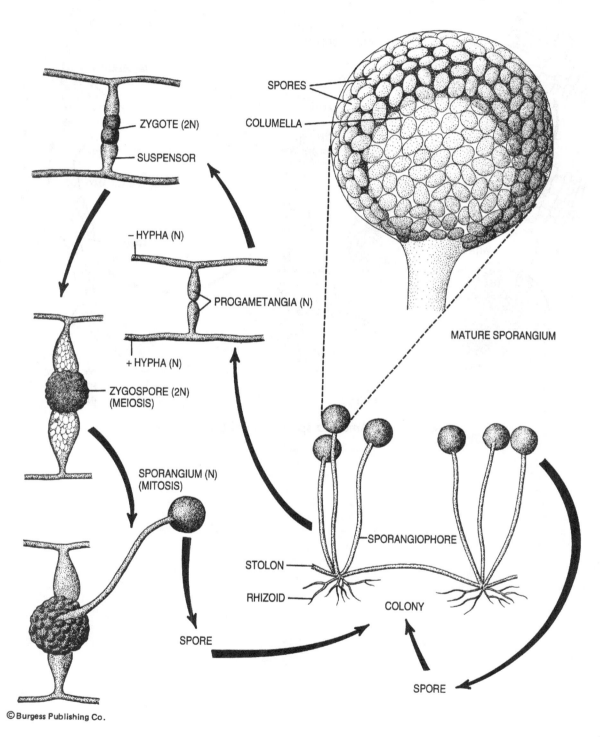

Rhizopus, a typical zygomycete.

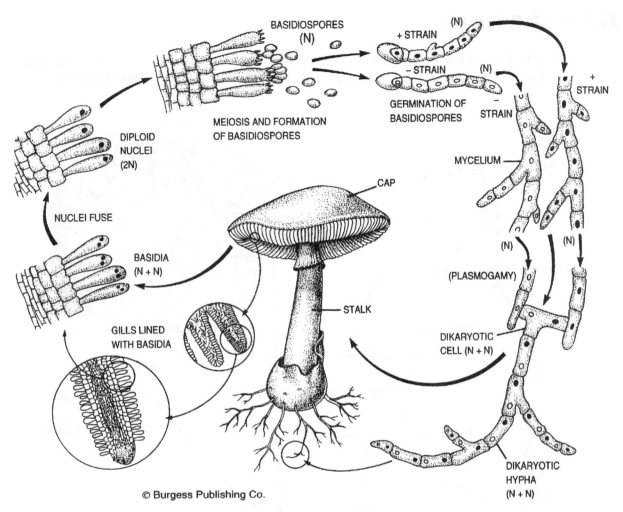

BASIDIOSPORES
(N)

+ STRAIN

- STRAIN

(N)

+ STRAIN

(N)

MEIOSIS AND FORMATION
OF BASIDIOSPORES

GERMINATION OF
BASIDIOSPORES

- STRAIN

DIPLOID
NUCLEI
(2N)

MYCELIUM

NUCLEI FUSE

CAP

(N)

(N)

BASIDIA
(N + N)

(PLASMOGAMY)

STALK

GILLS LINED
WITH BASIDIA

DIKARYOTIC
CELL (N + N)

DIKARYOTIC
HYPHA
(N + N)

© Burgess Publishing Co.

Life cycle of *Amanita* sp. A typical Basidiomycete.

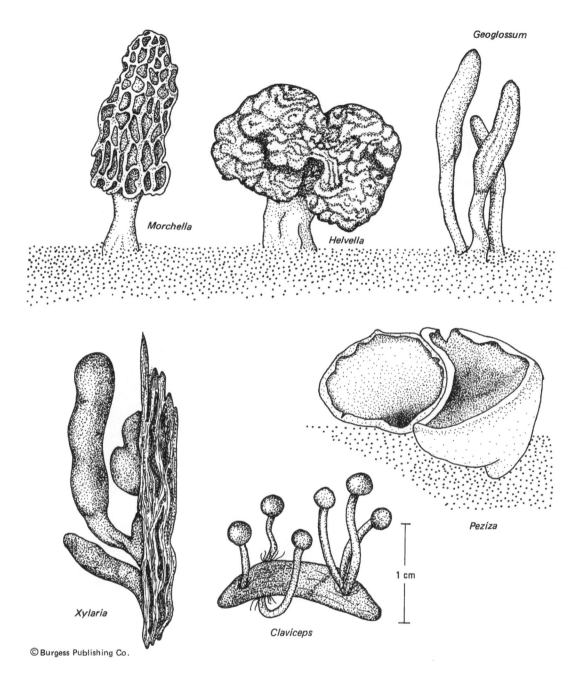

Morchella

Helvella

Geoglossum

Peziza

Xylaria

Claviceps

1 cm

© Burgess Publishing Co.

Typical forms of reproductive structures of the Ascomycetes. See the example life cycle on display in the lab.

EXERCISE 4 LICHENS

Lichens are the ultimate example of a mutualistic symbiotic organism. Observe various examples of lichens and be able to identify the three major growth forms—oliose, fruticose and crustose. MANY OF THESE MAY BE FOUND IN YOUR STUDY PLOTS.

CHAPTER 15 REVIEW QUESTIONS (2 POINTS EACH)

Name_____

1.   What are the three groups of fungi you observed in lab today?

2.   What are the three types of lichens set out for you to observe?

3.   _____ is a flagellated protista you observed in
        lab.

4.   What organism contains the symbiotic ciliates you observed using a compound
        microscope?

5.   Of the organisms you observed today which of these could be found growing on
        bare rock?

16
DOMAIN EUKARYA, KINGDOM PLANTAE

OBJECTIVES

Observe several examples of the **Chlorobionta,** from the primitive green algae (chlorophyta) to the spore bearing ferns that later gave rise to the seed plants.

Describe and identify stages in the life cycle of spore bearing plants.

Develop a better understanding of the evolution of vascular and nonvascular spore bearing plants.

BACKGROUND INFORMATION

The Chlorobionta is a monophyletic group traditionally called the green algae (chlorophyta) plus the land plants (embryophytes). The green algae alone are a paraphyletic group. Several apomorphies unite the chlorobionts. All chlorobionts contain chloroplasts that are different from those of the other photosynthetic organisms because they contain **chlorophyll b** in addition to chlorophyll a. Because all land plants have identical chloroplasts with respect to this feature, this chloroplast type is thought to represent a major apomorphy uniting all chlorobionts. The storage compound of this group is true starch (amylose), a polymer of glucose units. Green plants also have unique flagella characteristics and most have cell walls made of cellulose, a polymer of beta-1-4 glucose units.

Green algae occur in a variety of morphological forms. Most have flagellated motile cells at one phase of their life cycle. Green algae are found in fresh and marine waters; some are found in soil or moist terrestrial habitats. Within the lineage giving rise to land plants, certain innovations in reproductive structures appear to be pre-adaptations to survival on land. One of these involves the evolution of **oogamy,** a type of sexual reproduction in which one gamete, the **egg,** becomes larger and non-flagellated. The other gamete is, by default, called a sperm cell. Oogamy is found in all land plants and, by independent evolution, in all animals including humans.

Green algae that reproduce through oogamy gave rise to land plants that reproduce by the production of spores and eventually seeds. We will explore how this diverse and successful lineage

PROCEDURE

EXERCISE #1

Observe specimens of green algae and note the adaptations and pre-adaptations that allowed for the colonization of land. Note the lifecycle and the advent of oogamy.

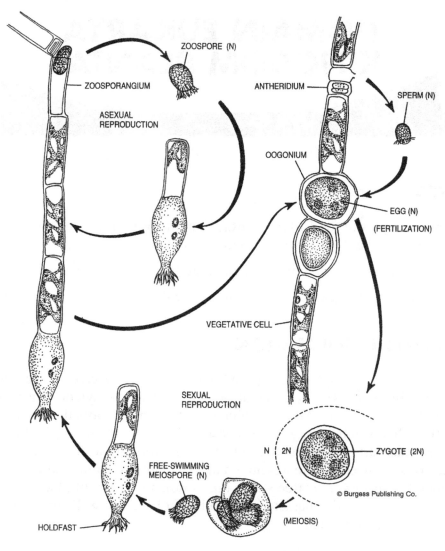

Oogamy in a Green Alga

evolved to cope with a changing environment. Several major changes occurred to primitive plants some 400 million years ago that enabled them to move from an aquatic to a terrestrial environment. These changes included the evolution of a life cycle in which a haploid phase (the **gametophyte**) alternates with a diploid phase (the **sporophyte**); such plant life cycles are often described by the phrase **alternation of generations.** The sporophyte generation produces spores from which develop the gametophyte generation. The gametophyte generation produces gametes which fuse and develop into the sporophyte generation. In the more advanced forms of the land plants, the visible plant body is the diploid sporophyte generation. The visible plant body in the less advanced forms is the gametophyte generation. An advantage of the sporophyte is an increase in spore numbers, which may increase the possibility of genetic variation. Another major apomorphy of all land plants is the presence of an **embryo.** The embryo is defined as the immature sporophyte that is attached to, or surrounded by, the gametophyte. In seed bearing land plants, the embryo develops within the seed, a protective and food storage structure. The evolution of true **parenchyma tissues** and **apical growth** are other important events in plant evolution; all land plants share these characteristics. A third characteristic found in all land plants is the **cuticle,** which is a protective waxy layer on the outermost cells that aids in retention of water. The development of **antheridia** (specialized structures for protecting male gametes in a non-aquatic environment) and **archegonia** (specialized structures for protecting female gametes in a non-aquatic environment) were the next major steps in the evolution of land plants. An additional event was the development of **stomata** (guard cells). These are specialized epidermal cells on leaves and sometimes stems that aid in gas exchange and water retention.

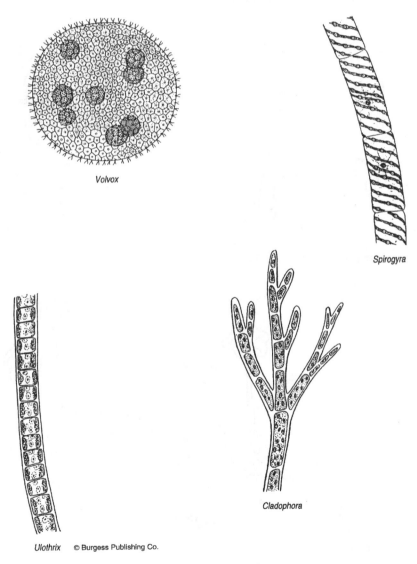

Volvox

Spirogyra

Cladophora

Ulothrix © Burgess Publishing Co.

Common Green Algae

The chlorobionts vary a great deal in size, shape, and habitat, but all produce some type of spore during their life cycle. Additionally, the more primitive forms produce a motile spore; this characteristic is lacking in most derived forms. Motility of gametes is a characteristic associated with organisms that require a moist environment in order to survive.

LIVERWORTS, HORNWORTS. THE FIRST LAND PLANTS

The **Bryophyta** represent a small and relatively inconspicuous group of land plants; they lack a vascular system, true leaves, stems and roots, which limits their distribution and ability to survive in many environments. They are usually found in moist environments, as their motile sperm require water to travel to the female reproductive structure to fertilize the egg. Bryophytes, however, are able to survive long periods of desiccation. When Bryophytes evolved true soil was not present. The earliest Bryophytes colonized bare rock. Their metabolic activities eventually led to the decomposition of the rock surface resulting in the formation of a thin layer of soil.

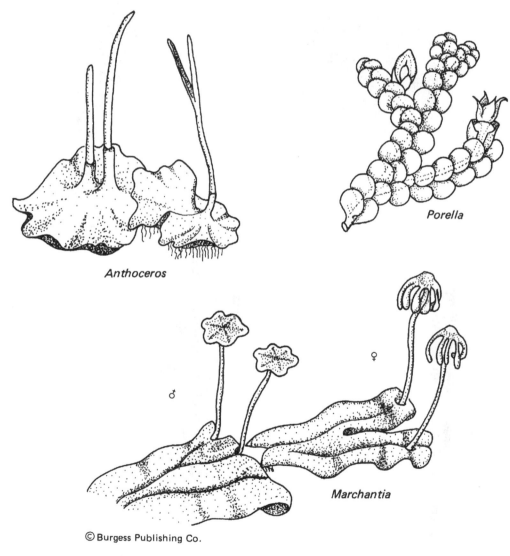

Anthoceros

Porella

Marchantia

Typical Hornwort, Leafy Liverwort, and Thaloid Liverwort

MOSSES (DIVISION BRYOPHYTA)

Moss species are characterized by their small size and association with moist habitats. The gametophyte is composed of a root-like structure called the **rhizome** and structures that resemble true stems and leaves, but do not have the same internal structure. **Archegonium** and ovules can be found at the apex of female plants. Male plants have **antheridia** that produce sperm at the apex. Meiosis occurs in the sporangium prior to the development of spores. The gametophyte is the conspicuous generation that consists of leaf-like structures arranged spirally around a stem-like axis and anchored to the substrate by **rhizoids.**

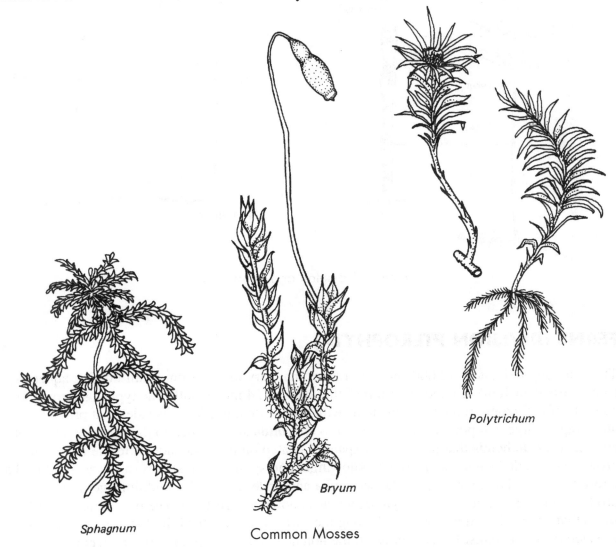

Polytrichum

Bryum

Sphagnum

Common Mosses

CLUB-MOSSES, HORSETAILS, WHISK FERNS AND FERNS; VASCULAR (TRACHEOPHYTES)

Vascular plants are more derived than mosses in three ways: 1) the sporophyte is the dominant generation, 2) the vascular tissue contains **xylem** and **phloem** and 3) the sporophyte has true leaves, roots and stems. These adaptations allow vascular plants to grow larger and live in more extreme environments, than most of the Bryophytes.

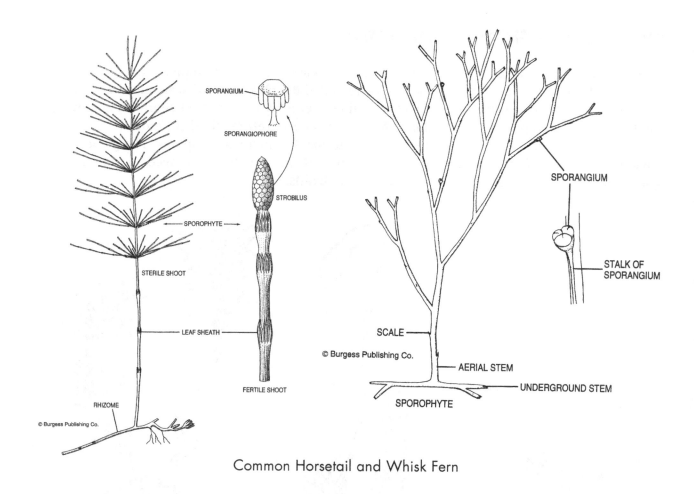

Common Horsetail and Whisk Fern

FERNS (DIVISION PTEROPHYTA)

There are approximately 12,000 species of ferns that vary in size from small floating aquatic forms (less than 1cm) to large "tree ferns" that may be 24 meters tall! The typical sporophyte consists of a **rhizome** (underground stem) with roots extending from its sides that provide anchorage. Large compound leaves referred to as **fronds** are attached to the rhizome and often emerge as **fiddleheads** that uncoil and expand. Located on the underside of fertile fronds are brown spots called **sori,** which contain **sporangia** and spores. Meiospores (n spores produced as a result of meiosis) are shot from the sporangia and under favorable conditions germinate to produce small green heart-shaped gametophytes known as **prothalli.** The prothallus has **rhizoids** that anchor it to the substrate. Among the rhizoids are **antheridia** that are spherical and elevated on short stalks. Located close to the notched end of the prothallus are **archegonia** which are flask-shaped female reproductive structures. Sperm formed in the **antheridia** have flagella and swim to the archegonia when water is present. After fertilization only one zygote develops into a sporophyte on any prothallus. The first generation sporophyte is generally small, while full-sized fronds will develop from persisting rhizomes in coming years.

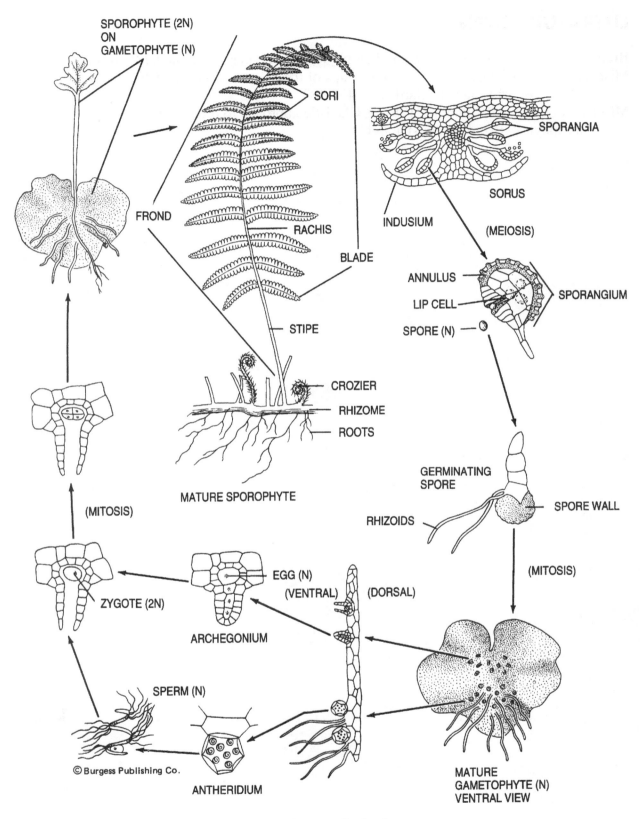

SPOROPHYTE (2N)
ON
GAMETOPHYTE (N)

SORI

SPORANGIA

SORUS

FROND

INDUSIUM

(MEIOSIS)

RACHIS

ANNULUS

LIP CELL

BLADE

SPORANGIUM

STIPE

SPORE (N)

CROZIER

RHIZOME

ROOTS

GERMINATING
SPORE

SPORE WALL

RHIZOIDS

(MITOSIS)

MATURE SPOROPHYTE

(MITOSIS)

EGG (N)
(VENTRAL)

(DORSAL)

ZYGOTE (2N)

ARCHEGONIUM

SPERM (N)

MATURE
GAMETOPHYTE (N)
VENTRAL VIEW

© Burgess Publishing Co.

ANTHERIDIUM

Typical Fern Life Cycle

LITERATURE CITED

Bremer, K. 1985. Summary of green plant phylogeny and classification. Cladistics 1(4):369-385.

Mischer et al, 1994. Phylogenetic relationships of the "Green Algae" and "Bryophytes" annals of the Missouri Botanical Garden 81:451-483

Mischer B.D, and S.P. Churchill 1984. A Cladistic approach to the phylogeny of the "Bryophytes" Brittonia 36(4):406-424

CHAPTER 16 REVIEW QUESTIONS (2 POINTS EACH)

Name_____

1.   Draw a diagram of *Spirogyra.*

2.   What is the name of the organism that has sori?

3.   What are the small structures called that are scattered over the surface
        of some liverworts?

4.   On the Wisk Fern what is the name of the small scale-like flaps of tissue?

5.   Of the organisms you observed today which one would contain silica deposits?

17

DOMAIN EUKARYA, KINGDOM PLANTAE SEED BEARING PLANTS: SPERMATOPHYTA

OBJECTIVES

Describe and identify features of angiosperms and gymnosperms

Understand life cycles of angiosperms and gymnosperms

Identify the parts and understand the function of seeds and flowers

BACKGROUND INFORMATION

Seed plants have a well developed vascular system that provides support for roots, stems and leaves as well as transport of materials. Reproduction via a seed provides a major advantage to land plants over spore producing plants, as seeds have a protective coat and a supply of food (**endosperm**) available for the embryo during its development. In addition, seeds may remain dormant until optimum conditions occur for germination and subsequent growth. The seed has made it possible for **angiosperms** and **gymnosperms** to become the dominant plants on earth. Seed plants are classified into two groups; first, the more primitive **gymnosperms** (naked seed) that produce seeds on the surface of the modified leaves that make up cones and, second, the derived **angiosperms** (hidden seed) that produce flowers and seed enclosed in fruit.

Seed plant sporophytes produce two kinds of meiospores, **microspores** (haploid male spores) and **megaspores** (haploid female spores). Microspores develop in **microsporangia** and become pollen grains that are self-contained **male gametophytes.** Megaspores are formed within the **megasporangia** then develop into **female gametophytes** or the ovule. Pollination is the process in which pollen grains are transferred to the female gametophyte. After coming in contact with the female gametophyte, the pollen grain develops into the male gametophyte with a **pollen tube** that provides a passage way for **sperm nuclei** to come into contact with the **egg** resulting in fertilization (zygote).

GYMNOSPERMS

Exposed seeds are produced on scale like structures in cones (**strobili**). Gymnosperms produce microspores on male cones and megaspores on female cones. Each form microscopic gametophytes that are dependent upon the large, free-living sporophyte. Gymnosperm sporophytes may be trees, shrubs, or vines. In this laboratory we will discuss the phyla Coniferophyta, Cycadophyta, Gnetophyta and Ginkgophyta but only the pine life cycle will be studied in detail.

CONIFEROPHYTA: CONIFERS

Coniferophyta are the most abundant gymnosperms in the temperate regions of the world and are commonly referred to as conifers. This group of cone bearing plants includes the Costal Redwood (*Sequoia sempervirens*) that is the tallest living vascular plant and the bristlecone pine (*Pinus aristata*) that is the oldest living vascular plant. The division also includes the fir, spruce, cedar, cypress and others. Conifers are able to tolerate dry climates because of a well developed vascular system and the presence of needle like leaves that restrict water loss. Conifers are of great economic value in the timber industry.

EXERCISE 1. PINE (*PINUS*):

Observe the specimens and slides of the pine needle and typical dicot leaves. In your notebook compare and contrast the various tissues and their locations. Leaves of conifers are waxy and somewhat thick; these features should help the leaf to conserve water.

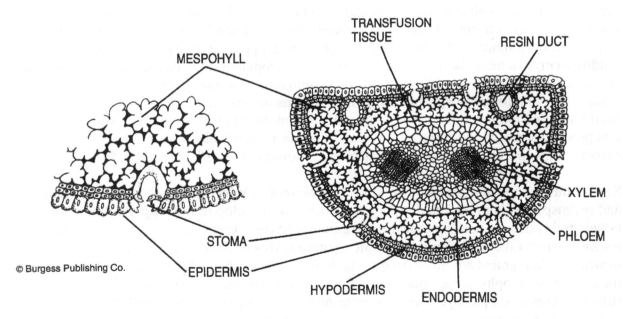

© Burgess Publishing Co.

Pine leaf, cross section

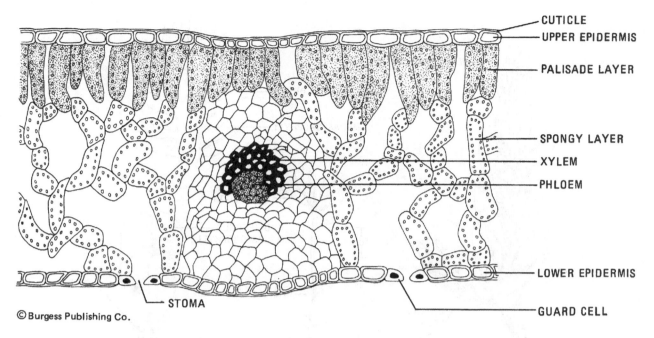

CUTICLE
UPPER EPIDERMIS
PALISADE LAYER
SPONGY LAYER
XYLEM
PHLOEM
LOWER EPIDERMIS
GUARD CELL
STOMA

© Burgess Publishing Co.

Dicot leaf, cross section

STAMINATE CONES (MALE), AND OVULATE CONES: (FEMALE):

Demonstration slides and live specimens will be available. Note the location of male and female cones and also, the location of the seeds.

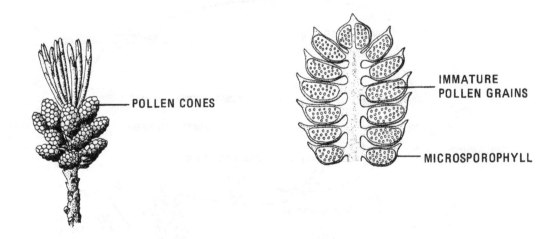

POLLEN CONES

IMMATURE
POLLEN GRAINS

MICROSPOROPHYLL

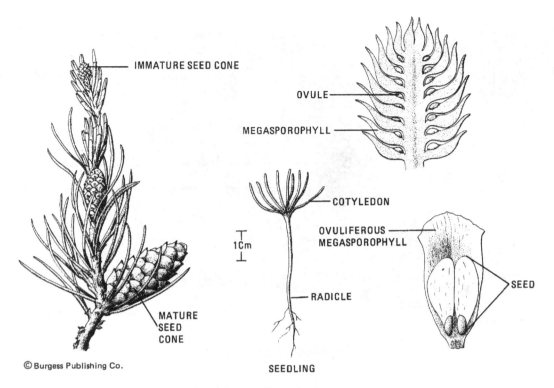

Pine Reproduction Structures

PINE LIFE CYCLE:

Note the different structures in this life cycle. Recreate this life cycle in your lab notebook with all the structures labeled. Also indicated where meiosis and fertilization takes place.

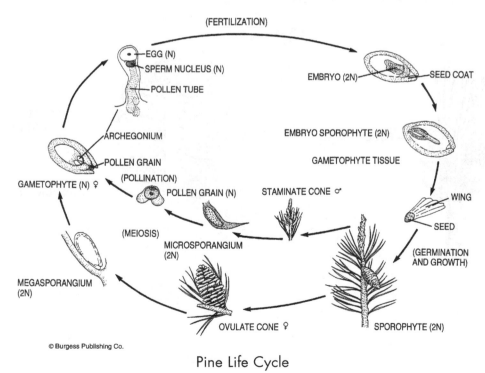

Pine Life Cycle

ANGIOSPERMS: PHYLUM ANTHROPHYTA

This group of flowering plants is the most diversified, abundant and widespread of all plants. There is much variation in size from 1 mm to 100 m in height. Like gymnosperms, angiosperms have a major impact on the world economy (food and fiber for humans). Angiosperms can be divided into monocots and dicots. Monocots have one cotyledon (seed leaf), flower parts are in sets of three, leaf and petal venation is parallel, vascular bundles form multiple rings and monocots lack a true vascular cambium. Dicots have two cotyledons, flower parts are in sets of four or five, leaf venation is reticulate, vascular bundles form one ring or cylinder, and dicots have a true vascular cambium.

BACKGROUND INFORMATION:

Flowers vary significantly in size, shape, color and structure and for that reason only a typical flower will be studied in this laboratory session.

The typical complete flower is composed of sepals, petals, stamens, and carpels. Sepals are often green and since they are outermost they protect the flower from adverse conditions. Collectively, the sepals make up the **calyx.** Petals are found within the calyx and known collectively as the **corolla.** The calyx and corolla combined form the perianth. Stamens (the male part of the plant) are found within the perianth and produce pollen within their anthers. Carpels, distinct sections of the ovary to which the ovules are attached, are located within a cavity called a locule. The **ovary** along with the stigma and style form the female reproductive structure called the **pistil.** Following fertilization the ovary will develop into a fruit which contains the seed(s).

Fertilization, the fusing of a male and a female **gamete** (specialized reproductive cells) to form a **zygote** (a single cell that will develop into an embryo), occurs in both animals and plants, but the process in flowering plants is different from that in animals. Angiosperms reproduce by a process called **double fertilization.** In double fertilization two haploid (n) sperm are formed in each pollen grain and the ovule or mature embryo sac consists of a single large cell containing 8 haploid nuclei. Five of these nuclei usually breakdown. One of the haploid sperm fuses with a haploid megaspore in the embryo sac forming the diploid (2n) zygote. The other haploid sperm fuses with two haploid nuclei (polar nuclei) in the ovule to form a triploid (3n) tissue that becomes the endosperm and serves as a food source for the developing embryo.

The flower sits on a bulbous shaped structure called a receptacle. The flower and receptacle are often located at the end of a stalk-like structure, the peduncle.

The perianth of a flower is used by botanist to describe flower types. A flower which is radically symmetrical and all parts of the perianth are similar in size and shape is said to be a **regular** flower. If the flower is bilaterally symmetrical and perianth parts are not alike, the flower is said to be **irregular.**

A flower that has sepals, petals, stamens, and carpels is said to be **complete.** If a flower is missing one or more of these four parts it would be considered **incomplete.** A flower that has stamens (male organs) and carpels (female organs) is considered **perfect;** an **imperfect** flower would have only one of these structures.

The development from zygote to embryo involves several stages.

A fruit is defined as a mature, ripened ovary that may or may not have accessory parts of the flower. Dry fruit may break open as they mature releasing seeds. Seed of plants with fleshy fruit remain within the fruit until germination or are dispersed as animals eat the fruit and scatter the seeds or the seeds are ingested and pass through the animals digestive tract.

Typically the outer wall of the fruit, the **pericarp,** is composed of an **exocarp** (outer), **mesocarp** (middle), and **endocarp** (inside). Seed (ovules) are located within the pericarp as are partitions and placental tissue. It is not uncommon for the receptacle to constitute a large portion of a fruit. Simple fleshy fruits include the drupe, berry and pome. Complex, fleshy fruits are either aggregate or multiple carpels.

EXERCISE 2 THE FLOWER:

Observe the fresh and preserved flower specimens. Flowers are reproductive shoots usually composed of four main parts: sepals, corolla, stamens, and pistil. Recreate this flower in your lab notebook and label all structures.

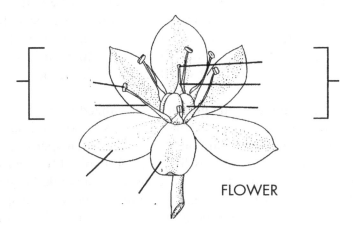

FLOWER

ALTERNATION OF GENERATIONS

Study the general life cycle of a flowering plant and recreate it in your lab notebook with all the structures labeled. Also, indicate where meiosis and fertilization occurs.

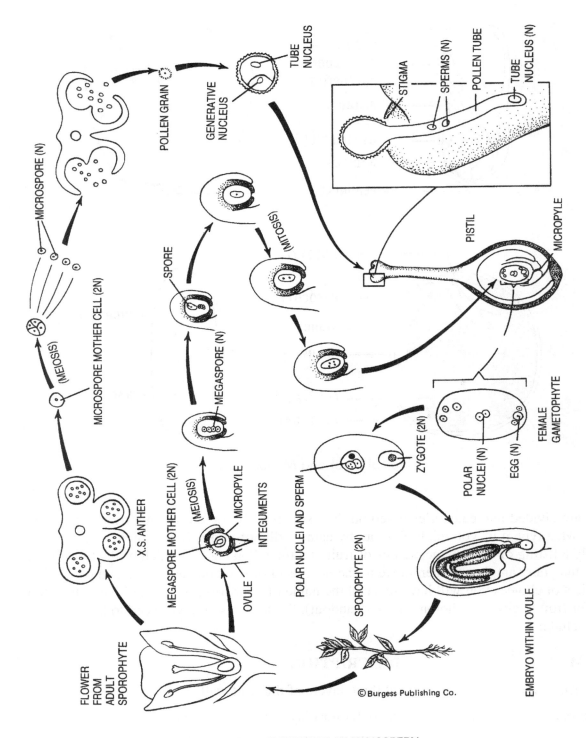

GENERALIZED LIFE CYCLE OF AN ANGIOSPERM

The following labels appear within the figure:

TUBE NUCLEUS

POLLEN GRAIN

GENERATIVE NUCLEUS

MICROSPORE (N)

STIGMA
SPERMS (N)
POLLEN TUBE
TUBE NUCLEUS (N)

(MITOSIS)

SPORE

MICROSPORE MOTHER CELL (2N)

(MEIOSIS)

MEGASPORE (N)

PISTIL

MICROPYLE

(MEIOSIS)

X.S. ANTHER

MEGASPORE MOTHER CELL (2N)

MICROPYLE

OVULE

INTEGUMENTS

POLAR NUCLEI AND SPERM

ZYGOTE (2N)

FEMALE GAMETOPHYTE

POLAR NUCLEI (N)

EGG (N)

SPOROPHYTE (2N)

FLOWER FROM ADULT SPOROPHYTE

EMBRYO WITHIN OVULE

© Burgess Publishing Co.

EXERCISE 3 SEED:

Observe the seeds (dry and soaked) and the prepared slides of various seeds. Note any differences between a monocot and dicot seed. The seed contains stored nutrients that are used by germinating plant embryos and serve as a food source for animals and humans.

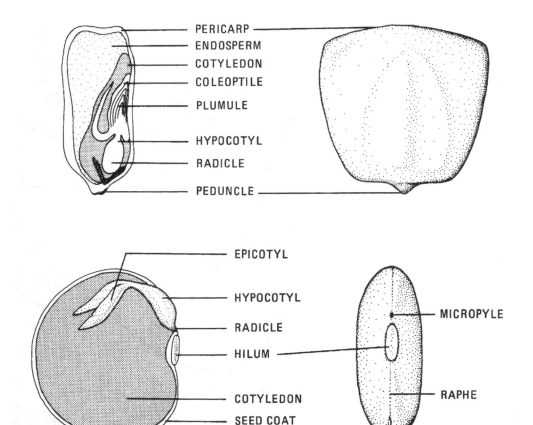

PERICARP
ENDOSPERM
COTYLEDON
COLEOPTILE
PLUMULE

HYPOCOTYL
RADICLE

PEDUNCLE

EPICOTYL

HYPOCOTYL

RADICLE

HILUM

COTYLEDON
SEED COAT

MICROPYLE

RAPHE

Typical Dicot and Monocot Seeds

Fruit are divided into categories based on their structure. If you are given a fruit and do not know what type it is, you might find out by using a **dichotomous key.** A dichotomous key is simply a listing of two characteristics of fruit at a time. You choose which of the two characteristics fits your sample and then move to the next level of two choices. At the end of the list of couplets of choices you will have reached the name of your fruit. An example of a dichotomous key for fruit is given (dichotomous key handout). Some terms you will need to know to use this key include:

TERM	**DESCRIPTION**
pericarp............................	all three layers of the fruit wall
exocarp.............................	the outermost layer of the fruit wall
mesocarp..........................	the middle region of the fruit wall
endocarp..........................	the innermost layer of the fruit wall
dehiscent..........................	fruit splits open at maturity
indehiscent......................	fruit does not split open at maturity

FRUIT IDENTIFICATION

Use the dichotomous key to identify the samples of fruit provided.

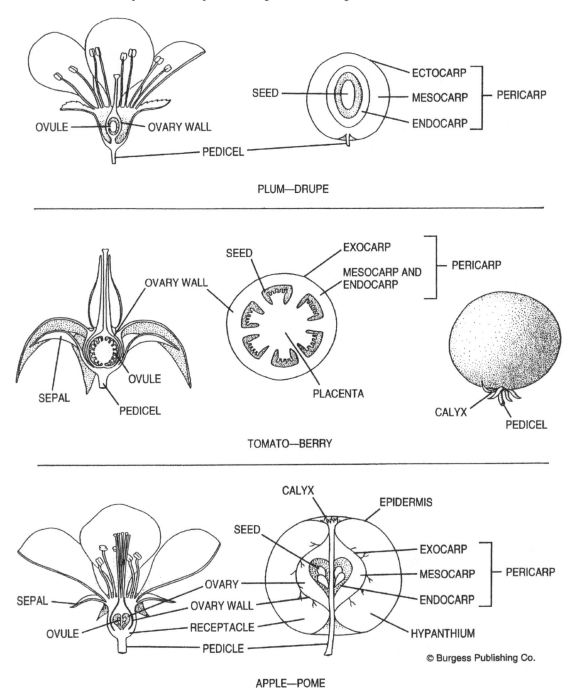

PLUM—DRUPE

TOMATO—BERRY

APPLE—POME

© Burgess Publishing Co.

REFERENCES CITED

Simpson M.G, E. W.A. Gergus and S. C. Mc Millan. 1998. The Lab Manual for Organismal
    Biology: an Evolutionary Approach. Burgess Publishing Inc 208 pp

CHAPTER 17 REVIEW QUESTIONS (2 POINTS EACH)

Name_____

1. Which organism is also referred to as a maidenhair tree because of its fan-shaped leaves?

2. What are the parts of the pistil (on a flower)?

3. What are of male parts of a flower?

4. What is an angiosperm called that has two cotyledons?

5. If a plants leaves have parallel veins would in be a monocot or dicot?

18
KINGDOM ANIMALIA

OBJECTIVES

Appreciate the diversity of animals. Describe the phylogenetic relationships among the members of the phylum and be able to give the major evidence that leads to the understanding of the relationships. Examine and compare the major characteristics of selected representatives from the following phyla: Porifera, Cnidaria, Platyhelminthes, Nematoda, Mollusca, Annelida, Anthropoda, Echinodermata, and Chordata. The study of the animal kingdom will take two laboratory periods. The first period will cover the "invertebrate" animals. The second will cover the "vertebrate" animals and will include the dissection of a small Mammal.

BACKGROUND

Members of the Kingdom Animalia are eukaryotic, multicellular, have diploid body cells, and pass through a blastula stage during embryonic development. Typically they are motile and use muscles to create the movement. Given these basic characteristics the diversity is amazing. The most primitive animals live in the oceans. Freshwater and terrestrial animals have evolved from various lineages. As you observe the animals on display look for evidences of **homology.** That is, look for body parts that have the same basic structure and embryological development, which are indicators of a common evolutionary history. Structures do not necessarily have to perform the same function to be homologous. In fact homologous structures often have evolved different functions as the result of minor structural changes.

The embryological developmental pattern characteristic of each phylum will be illustrated. The embryological development of animals is highly conservative and provides an excellent source of information on the evolutionary relationships among the phyla. Often two very different adult animals will have embryological developmental patterns that are essentially identical until late in the process.

In this laboratory you will study representatives of the major phyla. You should pay particular attention to three clusters of characteristics: (1) the adaptations of the musculoskeletal systems as they relate to locomotion. (2) The adaptations of the digestive systems for obtaining food by filtration or bulk ingestion. (3) The embryonic developmental pattern and larval form character-istic of the phyla as it relates to the phylogenetic relations of each group.

The Porifera and Cnidaria are more simple animals whose adult body is derived from two embryonic layers. The Platyhelminthes, Nematodes, Mollusca, Annelida, and Arthropoda have three embryonic layers and belong to the Protostome line of evolution. The Deuterostome line has given rise to the phyla the Echinodermata and the Chordata. There are other small phyla, which are not covered in this exercise.

LABORATORY ACTIVITIES

It is assumed that you have knowledge of the diagnostic characteristics of the major animal phyla. If you need a refresher, look in the appendix of your lecture text or for more detailed information refer to your lecture notes and the appropriate chapters of the text.

The laboratory period will be partitioned into three segments. The class will watch a video summarizing the major information concerning the phyla you will be studying in this laboratory period. Your group will make observations using microscope slides, preserved specimens and living specimens, when available. You should actively make observations, take notes, and discuss your understanding with other students. In the third segment, you will construct a den-drogram to summarize the relationships among the phyla of the Kingdom Animalia.

EXERCISE 1:

Watch the video. It emphasizes the invertebrate phyla.

EXERCISE 2:

Obtain a box of microscope slides for your group. You will visit designated areas to obtain speci-mens or to observe displays for each of the Phyla you are to study, and additional diagrams and instruction sheets. Identify the characteristics that are diagnostic of each phylum. You may want to refer to your textbook or class notes for additional information. Look carefully at the material. If there are models or living specimens on the front or side tables, the group should study them. Questions will be posed for each phylum that leads to the understanding of the musculoskeletal system, the nutritional adaptations, embryological development, and evolutionary relationships.

Determine what specific body parts are important in the locomotion of each animal. Determine the type of musculoskeletal system each animal possesses. Answer the question: how do mus-cles and support systems work together to produce the locomotion observed in each of the phyla you study? Determine from your observations the nutrient processing adaptation(s) for each ani-mal. Answer the questions posed for each phyla.

PHYLUM PORIFERA

The most primitive phylum we study is the Porifera, the sponges, whose body form is basically a sac-like pumping chamber formed of two cell layers. Examine the preserved specimens and study the diagrams. Determine the composition of the body wall. How many cell layers are present in the adult sponge? What gives the body of the sponge its form and support? These organisms are filter feeders. How do they create a feeding current and where is the filtered material trapped?

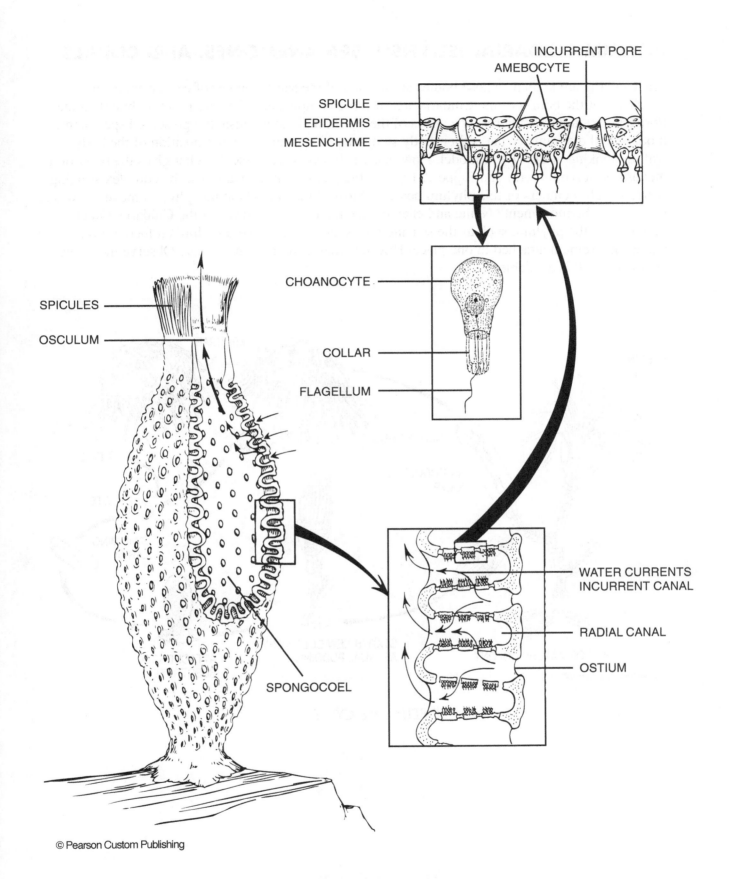

INCURRENT PORE
AMEBOCYTE
SPICULE
EPIDERMIS
MESENCHYME

CHOANOCYTE
COLLAR
FLAGELLUM

SPICULES
OSCULUM

SPONGOCOEL

WATER CURRENTS
INCURRENT CANAL

RADIAL CANAL

OSTIUM

SIMPLE SPONGE APPEARANCE, *GRANTIA*

PHYLUM CNIDARIA: JELLYFISH, SEA ANEMONES, AND CORALS

The Cnidaria are animals whose bodies are formed of the same number of cell layers as the Porifera, but the bodies of the Cnidaria are far more complex and they are more mobile than the Porifera. Examine the microscope slides of the *Hydra* and the medusa, the preserved specimens, models, and diagrams. What is their body symmetry? Determine the composition of the body wall by looking at the *Hydra* model. How many cell layers are present? What gives the body of a medusa or polyp its form and support? Look at the pictures of nematocysts, the complex stinging structures all members of this phylum possess. Most of the animals in this phylum move. How do they create the movement? Name and characterize the two body forms of the Cnidaria. Other members of the phylum, such as the sea anemones, are corals, have only limited locomotion as adults, and remain attached in one place. How can they colonize a new area? Observe the living *Hydra sp.,* if it is available.

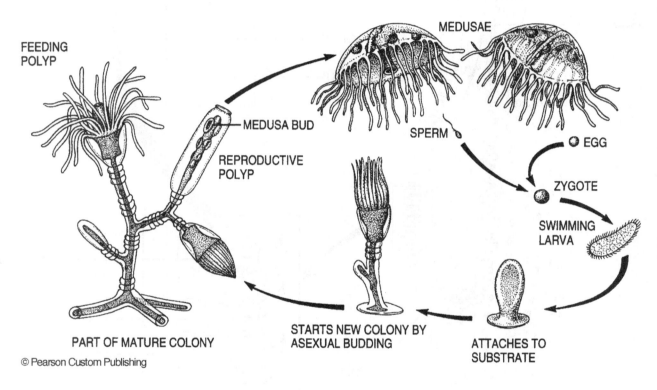

© Pearson Custom Publishing

OBELIA, LIFE CYCLE

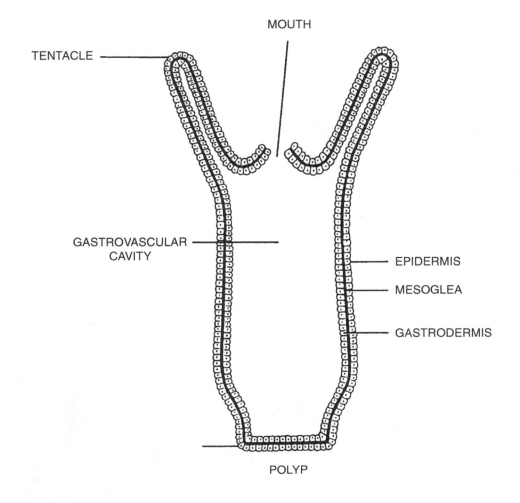

MOUTH

TENTACLE

GASTROVASCULAR
CAVITY

EPIDERMIS

MESOGLEA

GASTRODERMIS

POLYP

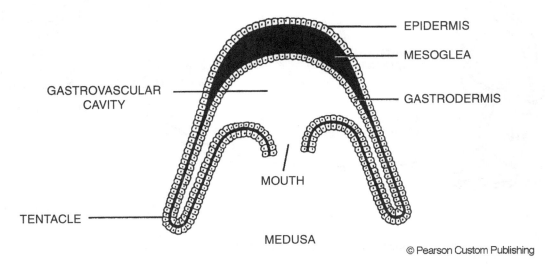

EPIDERMIS

MESOGLEA

GASTROVASCULAR
CAVITY

GASTRODERMIS

MOUTH

TENTACLE

MEDUSA

© Pearson Custom Publishing

Coelenterate Body Forms

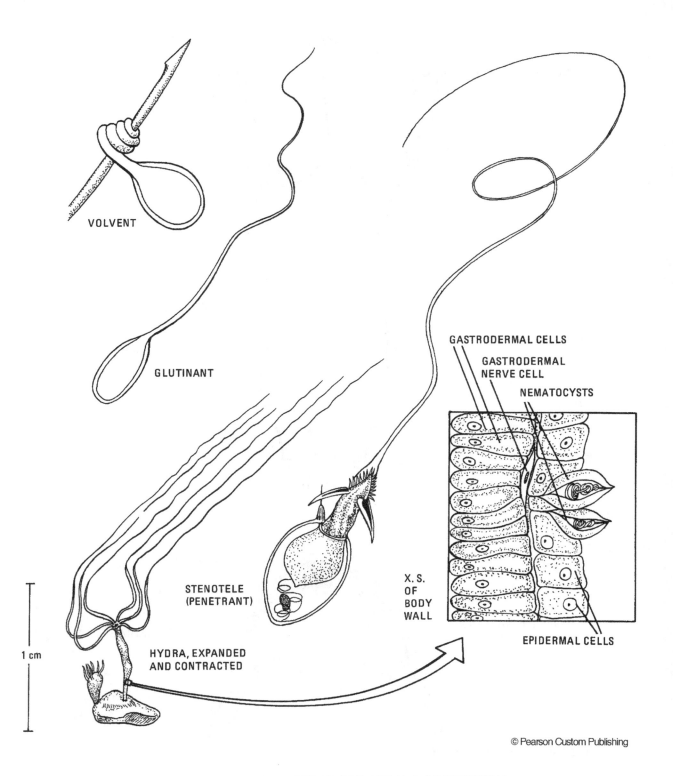

VOLVENT

GLUTINANT

STENOTELE
(PENETRANT)

HYDRA, EXPANDED
AND CONTRACTED

1 cm

GASTRODERMAL CELLS

GASTRODERMAL
NERVE CELL

NEMATOCYSTS

X. S.
OF
BODY
WALL

EPIDERMAL CELLS

© Pearson Custom Publishing

HYDRA, NEMATOCYSTS, APPEARANCE, AND X. S. OF BODY WALL

The **Protostome** line of evolution is characterized by embryological events that occur after the gastrula is formed. The next diagram illustrates a typical formation of a gastrula from the blastula. The **blastula** is a hollow ball formed by a single layer of cells. The **gastrula** stage begins as a two cell layered organism that gradually forms a third layer between the other two. These initial three cell layers are known as the primary embryonic germ layers and are called the **Ectoderm, Endoderm,** and **Mesoderm.** From their names can you determine where they are in the gastrula? Observe in the diagram that the gastrula is hollow, but that unlike the blastula the hollow center is open at the blastopore. In the Protostome line the blastopore becomes the mouth of the adult animal, hence the name Protostome or first mouth. The following phyla are the Protostome lineage.

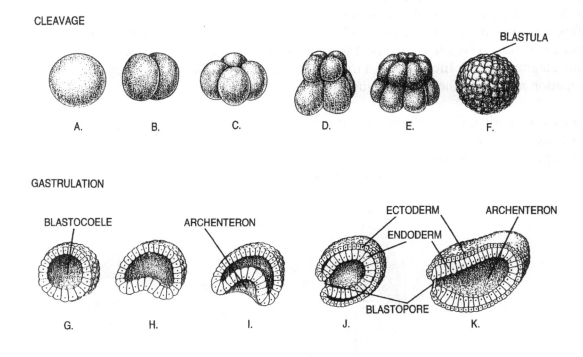

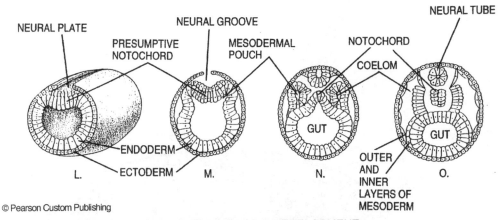

AMPHIOXIS, EARLY DEVELOPMENT

A typical animal blastula and gastrula

PHYLUM PLATYHELMINTHES: FLATWORMS

The evolution of three primary embryonic cell layers in the Platyhelminthes is a major evolutionary innovation that accompanied the development of bilateral symmetry and increased locomotor ability, in both speed and maneuverability.

Examine the preserved specimens, microscope slides, and the diagrams. What is the symmetry of flatworms? Determine the composition of the body wall. How many primary cell layers are present? What gives the body of these worms support? There are three classes in the phylum Platyhelminthes. Many of these worms are free-living and feed on dead organisms (Turbellaria). How do they ingest their food? Look at other members of this phylum that are parasitic, such as the flukes (Trematoda) and tapeworms (Cestoda). These organisms are internal parasites and cannot move themselves from one host to another. How can they parasitize a new host? Examine the diagrams of the life cycle of a trematode and cestode. Do these life cycles provide any information relative to the previous question?

Slides: Planarian, (Turbellaria) observe the body form and digestive tract.
A Fluke (Trematoda)
A Tapeworm (Cestoda)

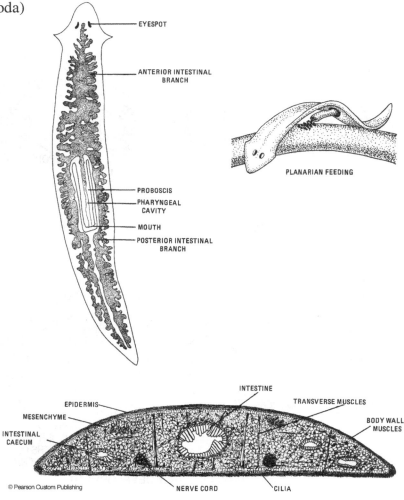

PLANARIAN FEEDING

PLANARIAN, APPEARANCE AND CROSS SECTION

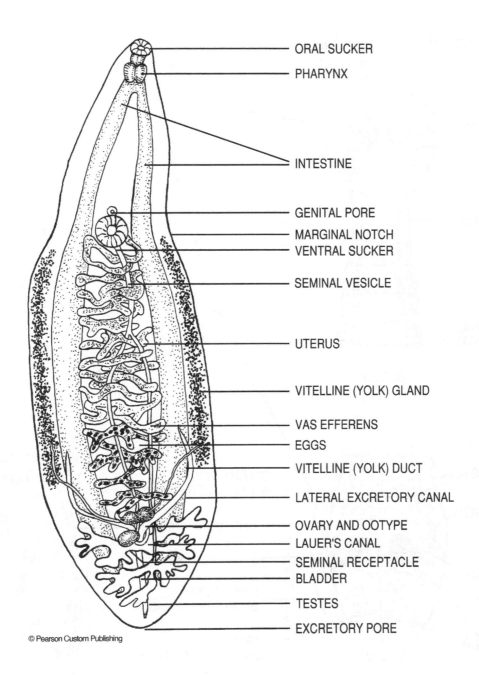

ORAL SUCKER

PHARYNX

INTESTINE

GENITAL PORE

MARGINAL NOTCH

VENTRAL SUCKER

SEMINAL VESICLE

UTERUS

VITELLINE (YOLK) GLAND

VAS EFFERENS

EGGS

VITELLINE (YOLK) DUCT

LATERAL EXCRETORY CANAL

OVARY AND OOTYPE

LAUER'S CANAL

SEMINAL RECEPTACLE

BLADDER

TESTES

EXCRETORY PORE

Opisthorchis, HUMAN LIVER FLUKE, GENERAL ANATOMICAL FEATURES

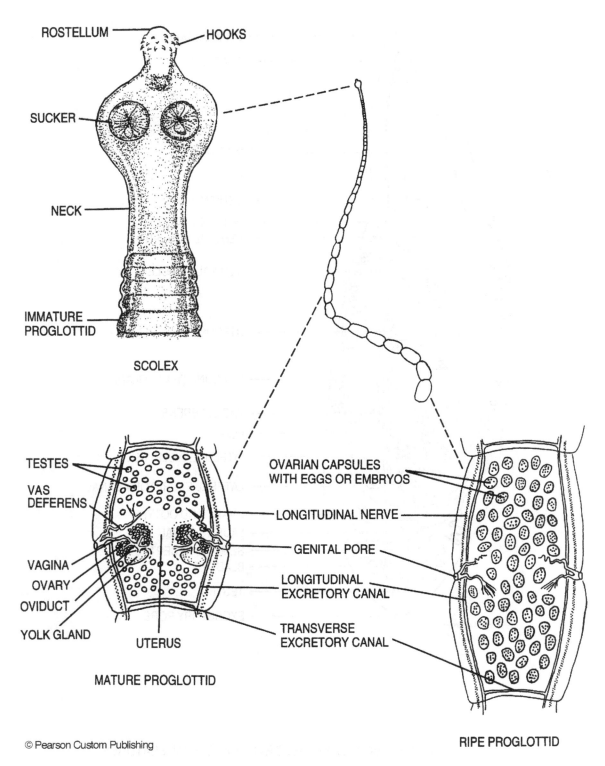

ROSTELLUM — HOOKS

SUCKER

NECK

IMMATURE PROGLOTTID

SCOLEX

TESTES

VAS DEFERENS

VAGINA
OVARY
OVIDUCT
YOLK GLAND
UTERUS

MATURE PROGLOTTID

OVARIAN CAPSULES WITH EGGS OR EMBRYOS

LONGITUDINAL NERVE

GENITAL PORE

LONGITUDINAL EXCRETORY CANAL

TRANSVERSE EXCRETORY CANAL

RIPE PROGLOTTID

© Pearson Custom Publishing

Dipylidium, DOG TAPEWORM, GENERAL ANATOMY

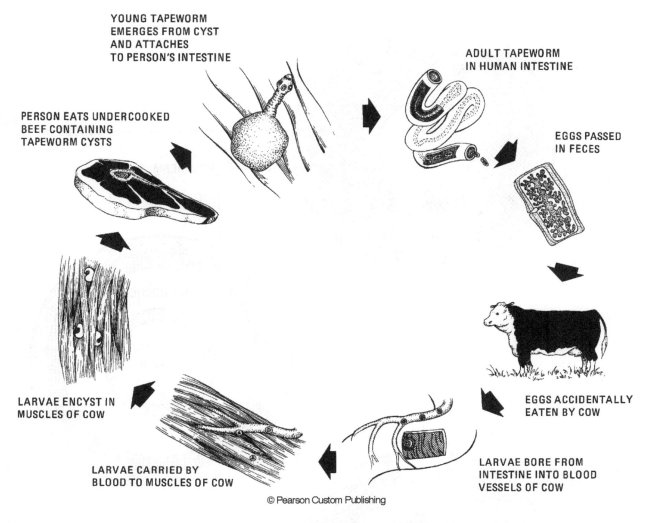

YOUNG TAPEWORM
EMERGES FROM CYST
AND ATTACHES
TO PERSON'S INTESTINE

ADULT TAPEWORM
IN HUMAN INTESTINE

PERSON EATS UNDERCOOKED
BEEF CONTAINING
TAPEWORM CYSTS

EGGS PASSED
IN FECES

LARVAE ENCYST IN
MUSCLES OF COW

EGGS ACCIDENTALLY
EATEN BY COW

LARVAE CARRIED BY
BLOOD TO MUSCLES OF COW

LARVAE BORE FROM
INTESTINE INTO BLOOD
VESSELS OF COW

© Pearson Custom Publishing

LIFE CYCLE OF BEEF TAPEWORM

PHYLUM NEMATODA AND ROTIFERA: ROUNDWORMS AND "WHEEL ANIMALS"

The next major evolutionary innovations are the body cavity (the coelom) and the tubular digestive tract with two openings. There are two forms of coelom. The pseudocoelom is not completely lined with a peritoneum derived from mesoderm and is characteristic of animals in the phyla **Nematoda** and **Rotifera.**

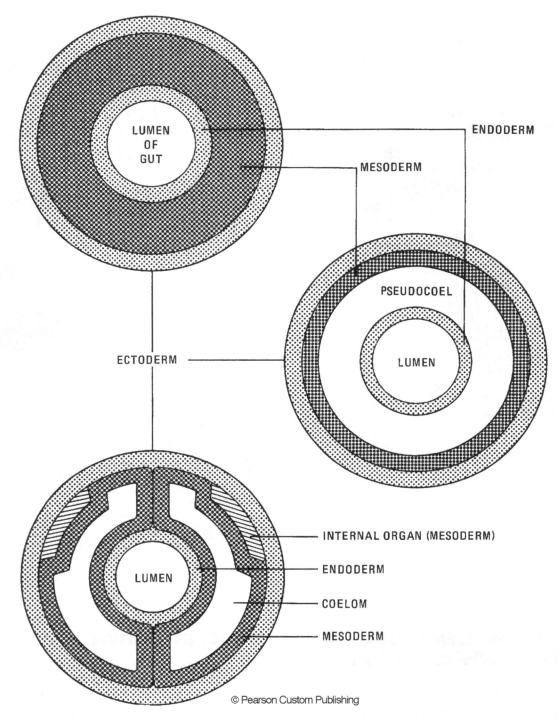

ENDODERM

MESODERM

PSEUDOCOEL

LUMEN
OF
GUT

LUMEN

ECTODERM

INTERNAL ORGAN (MESODERM)

ENDODERM

LUMEN

COELOM

MESODERM

© Pearson Custom Publishing

DIAGRAMMATIC CROSS SECTIONS,
BODY PLANES IN THE BILATERIA

Examine the microscope slide of a Nematode cross section and the coelom diagram to determine the composition of the body wall. How are the muscles oriented with respect to the body? How do the muscles operate with the pseudocoelom to create locomotion? How does Nematode locomotion compare to the locomotion in another coelomate worm phylum, the annelida? How does the Nematode locomotion compare with that of the other pseudocoelmate phylum, the Rotifera? Do these animals feed on living organisms or are they parasitic? How do they ingest their food? Do not generalize; these organisms have some specific adaptations. The digestive tract of these organisms has two openings. What is the advantage of two openings? Other members of these phyla are parasitic and cannot move from one host to another. How can they parasitize another host? Examine the diagram of the life cycle of a parasitic nematode. What is the biological role of such a complex life cycle?

Examine the living Nematodes and the living Rotifers. These are also pseudocoelomate animals that move by very different mechanisms. Look at the hydrostatic skeleton demonstration and the diagrams of the types of body cavities (coelom).

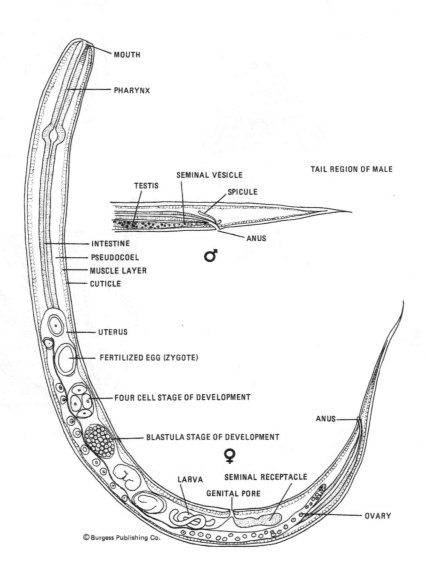

© Burgess Publishing Co.

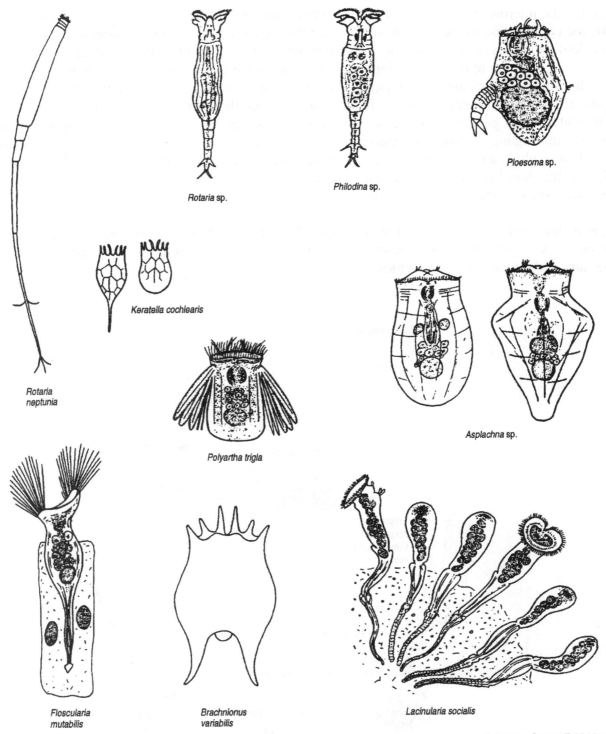

Rotaria sp.

Philodina sp.

Ploesoma sp.

Rotaria
neptunia

Keratella cochlearis

Polyartha trigla

Asplachna sp.

Floscularia
mutabilis

Brachnionus
variabilis

Lacinularia socialis

FRESH WATER ROTIFERS

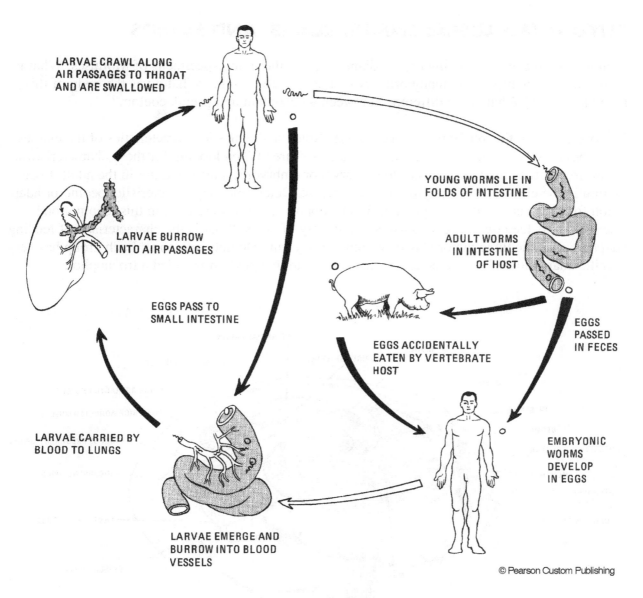

LARVAE CRAWL ALONG
AIR PASSAGES TO THROAT
AND ARE SWALLOWED

LARVAE BURROW
INTO AIR PASSAGES

EGGS PASS TO
SMALL INTESTINE

LARVAE CARRIED BY
BLOOD TO LUNGS

LARVAE EMERGE AND
BURROW INTO BLOOD
VESSELS

YOUNG WORMS LIE IN
FOLDS OF INTESTINE

ADULT WORMS
IN INTESTINE
OF HOST

EGGS ACCIDENTALLY
EATEN BY VERTEBRATE
HOST

EGGS
PASSED
IN FECES

EMBRYONIC
WORMS
DEVELOP
IN EGGS

© Pearson Custom Publishing

ASCARIS, LIFE CYCLE

THE ADVANCED PHYLA IN THE PROTOSTOME LINE OF EVOLUTION

The remaining groups of animals are coelomate (have a true coelom). At this point in evolution two major lines diverged. One of the lines continues as the advanced Protostome lineage that contains the major phyla the Annelida, Mollusca, and Anthropoda. In this group of phyla the evolution of segmentation occurred leading to a great diversity of body parts that are used for increased locomotion. Increased locomotion was critical to the successful invasion of the land and air.

PHYLUM MOLLUSCA: SNAILS, CLAMS, AND SQUIDS

Examine the preserved specimens, the diagrams, and the living specimens of Molluscs. What is their body symmetry? How many primary cell layers are present? What gives the body of this animal support? What is the difference between a eucoelom and pseudocoelom?

The organisms in this phylum are very diverse. Note the diagnostic characteristics of the classes in the phylum. What characteristics do the classes share? When looking for these characteristics, be aware that they may only appear in the larval or embryonic stages and not in the adult. Loco-motion in the classes of this phylum is very diverse. Determine the characteristic locomotor adap-tation for each class within the phylum. What support structures are used in this locomotion? These animals feed on living organisms in a variety of ways. What is the characteristic of feeding adaptation for the three major classes within the phylum? Do not generalize. Each group has very specific adaptations. The characteristic larva found in this phylum is called a trochophore.

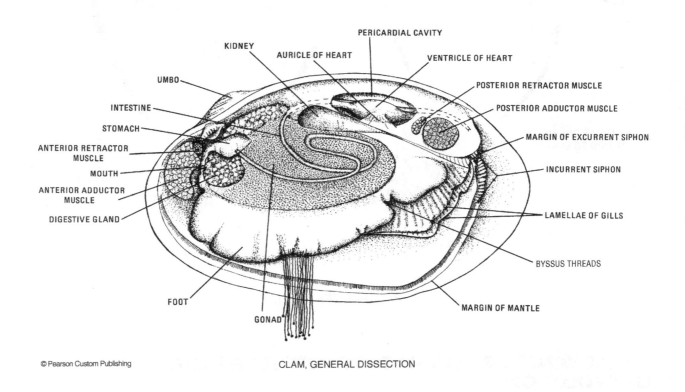

CLAM, GENERAL DISSECTION

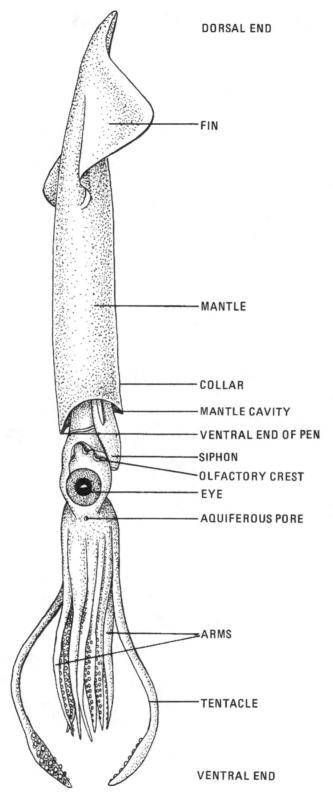

DORSAL END

FIN

MANTLE

COLLAR

MANTLE CAVITY

VENTRAL END OF PEN

SIPHON

OLFACTORY CREST

EYE

AQUIFEROUS PORE

ARMS

TENTACLE

VENTRAL END

SQUID, LATERAL VIEW

PHYLUM ANNELIDA: SEGMENTED WORMS

Examine the preserved specimens of the three classes: Oligochaetes, Polychaetes, and Hirudinea, the diagrams, and the living specimens if available. What is their body symmetry? What gives the body of these animals support?

The organisms in this phylum are not very diverse, however, they are grouped into three classes: the Polychaetes, Oligochaetes, and the Hirudinea. What characteristics do the members of the three classes share? Locomotion in the classes of this phylum requires the coelom. Examine how the muscles operate with the coelom to create locomotion by working the hydrostatic skeleton demonstration. How does this compare to the locomotor system in the other coelomate worm phylum, the Nematoda? The annelids feed on various types of living organisms or on decaying organic material. What are some of the feeding adaptations found within the phylum? The characteristic larva of the marine forms of this phylum is a Trochophore. This indicates it is a common ancestor with the Annelids.

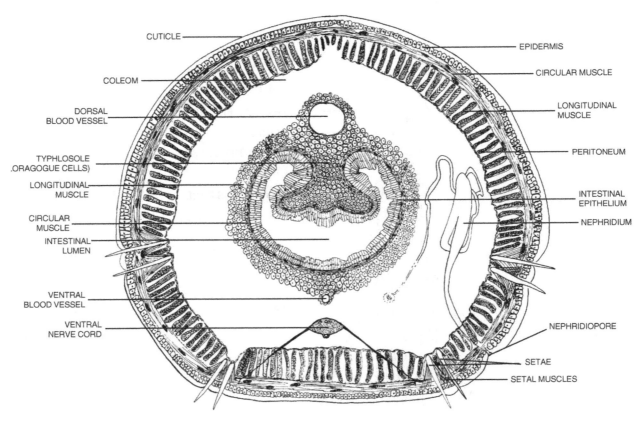

© Pearson Custom Publishing   CROSS SECTION OF EARTHWORM, *Lumbricus*

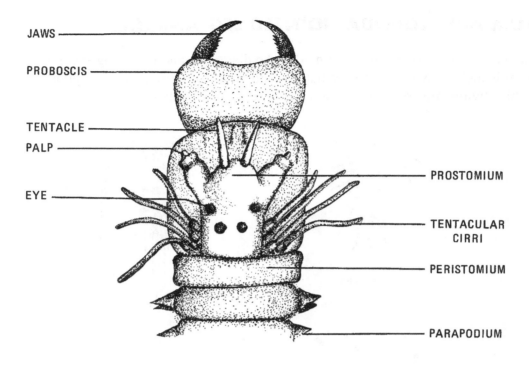

JAWS

PROBOSCIS

TENTACLE

PALP

EYE

PROSTOMIUM

TENTACULAR
CIRRI

PERISTOMIUM

PARAPODIUM

HEAD OF NEREIS

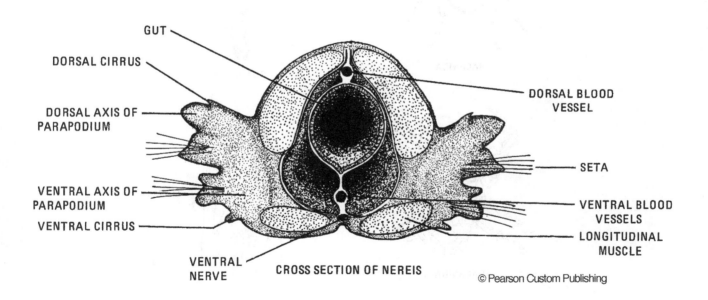

GUT

DORSAL CIRRUS

DORSAL AXIS OF
PARAPODIUM

VENTRAL AXIS OF
PARAPODIUM

VENTRAL CIRRUS

DORSAL BLOOD
VESSEL

SETA

VENTRAL BLOOD
VESSELS

LONGITUDINAL
MUSCLE

VENTRAL
NERVE

CROSS SECTION OF NEREIS

© Pearson Custom Publishing

Nereis, HEAD AND X.S. WITH PARAPODIA

PHYLUM ARTHROPODA: JOINTED-LEG ANIMALS

Examine the preserved specimens, the model, the diagrams, and the living specimens if available. What is their body symmetry? What gives the body of these animals support? The organisms in this phylum are very diverse. What characteristics do they share?

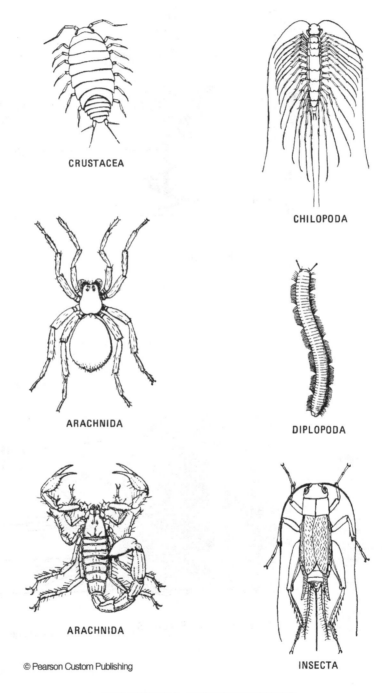

CRUSTACEA

CHILOPODA

ARACHNIDA

DIPLOPODA

ARACHNIDA

© Pearson Custom Publishing

INSECTA

ARTHROPODA, REPRESENTATIVES
OF MAJOR CLASSES

How does the musculoskeletal system create locomotion? How does this compare to the locomotion system in the other coelomate phyla? This very large group of animals is organized into
subphyla and classes. Observe the characteristics of each taxonomic group that is provided. The
animals in this phylum feed on living organisms or decaying material in an amazing variety of
ways. What characteristic structure is probably responsible for the amazing variety of locomotor
and feeding adaptations in this phylum? Note that many members of this phylum have been very
successful in adapting to the terrestrial environment and to flying. The characteristic larva of the
marine forms of this phylum is called a nauplius.

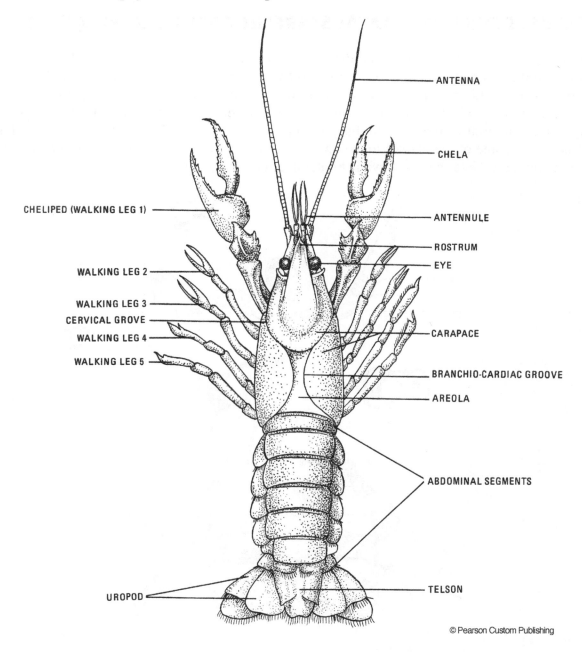

CRAYFISH, GENERAL DORSAL APPEARANCE

THE DEUTEROSTOME LINE OF EVOLUTION

The **Deuterostome** line has given rise to two major phyla, the Echinodermata and the Chordata. What is the diagnostic embryological characteristic of this line of evolution? (Hint, translate the word deuterostome.) The first of these phyla, the Echinodermata, lack segmentation, are slow moving, and display a secondary radial symmetry. The animals in the phylum Chordata are bilateral and have segmentation and have developed a wide range of adaptations.

PHYLUM ECHINODERMATA: STARFISH AND THEIR RELATIVES

Examine the preserved specimens and diagrams. What is their body symmetry and how does it differ from the symmetry of most other animals? What gives the body of this animals support? The organisms in this phylum are diverse, but limited to living only in salt water. What characteristics do they share? How does the skeletal system differ from that of the Anthropods? What unique structure do the organisms in this phylum possess? How is this structure functional for locomotion in some of the classes in the phylum? Examine the picture of the larva characteristic of the phylum. Note that the larva is bilateral, although the adults are not.

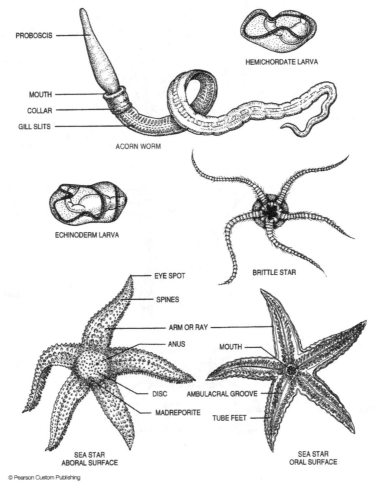

ECHINODERM AND HEMICHORDATE LARVAE,
ACORN WORM, AND SEA STARS

These animals feed on living organisms. Is there a characteristic feeding adaptation for the animals within the phylum? What are the characteristic developmental pattern and the larva in this phylum? This phylum is on a different line of evolution than other advanced invertebrate phyla. What evidence supports this statement?

PHYLUM CHORDATA

All members of the Phylum Chordata share three characteristics at some time in their life: (1) dorsal hollow nerve cord, (2) a notochord, and (3) pharyngeal gill slits. Some members of this group show all of these characteristics only during their embryological development. Embryological data suggests that the chordates probably evolved from a common ancestor they share with the Echinoderms.

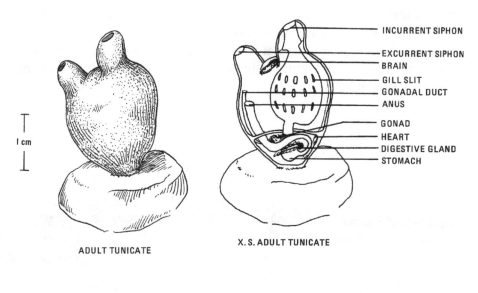

ADULT TUNICATE

X.S. ADULT TUNICATE

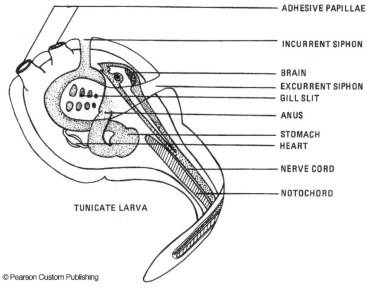

TUNICATE LARVA

© Pearson Custom Publishing

TUNICATE, STRUCTURE OF ADULT AND LARVA

The most primitive chordates are small marine organisms, the Urochordata. These animals do not appear to belong to the Phylum Chordata if only adult characteristics are considered. The adults are sessile, filter feeding animals called Tunicates. Their larvae, on the other hand, have all three of the chordate characteristics. Examine the pictures of the larva and adult Urochordate. Examine the preserved adult in the demonstration. Look for the three characteristics common to the members of the Phylum Chordata; are all present? What is the meaning of the prefix Uro-? Why are these animals named Urochordata?

A second primitive group of chordates, the Cephalochordata, have all three chordates characteristics as adults. Their notochord extends from the tail anteriorly to the very tip of the head hence the name Cephalochordata. Study the prepared microscope slide of the Lancet, Amphioxus sp. Observe the three chordate characteristics.

These two groups are termed the "invertebrate chordates" because they do not have a support structure around the spinal cord (the dorsal hollow nerve cord). As evolution continued in the chordates, support structures appeared lateral to and eventually surrounding the spinal cord. These support structures form the vertebral column. Those chordates with a vertebral column are called "vertebrate" chordates.

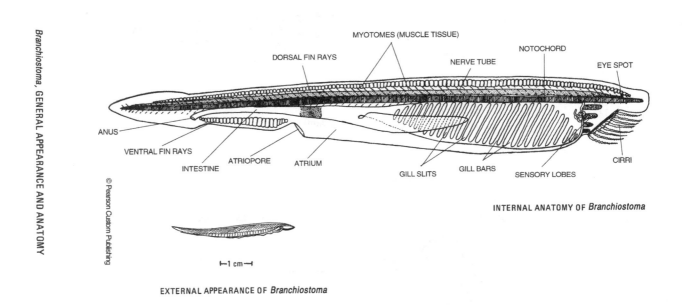

Branchiostoma, GENERAL APPEARANCE AND ANATOMY

© Pearson Custom Publishing

MYOTOMES (MUSCLE TISSUE)

DORSAL FIN RAYS
NERVE TUBE
NOTOCHORD
EYE SPOT

ANUS
VENTRAL FIN RAYS
INTESTINE
ATRIOPORE
ATRIUM
GILL SLITS
GILL BARS
SENSORY LOBES
CIRRI

INTERNAL ANATOMY OF *Branchiostoma*

⊢1 cm⊣

EXTERNAL APPEARANCE OF *Branchiostoma*

CHAPTER 18 REVIEW QUESTIONS (2 POINTS EACH)

Name_____

1.   A Chinese liver fluke would be found in which phylum?

2.   Which organism in lab today had corona that is used to gather food?

3.   A Nautilus would be found in which phylum?

4.   A sponge has feeding cells called _____.

5.   What is the name of the stinging structures that are found in the phylum *Cnidaria?*

19
THE VERTEBRATE CHORDATES

Since the Chordata is the phylum in which you belong, you will look at the diversity of vertebrate chordates in more detail. You will follow chordate evolution from aquatic to terrestrial, from terrestrial back to aquatic, and from terrestrial to aerial (flying) adaptations. You will also examine adaptations to three habitats: the aquatic, the terrestrial, and the arial.

The **aquatic environment,** either salt water or fresh water, provides support and the fluid needed for the maintenance of cell structure and function. The buoyant force exerted by the fluid that surrounds them supports organisms living in the aquatic environment. Their locomotor adaptations also make use of the fact that a dense liquid surrounds them. Their bodies do not require special covering to keep from losing water. The relative stability of the temperature and composition of the aquatic environment that surrounds them minimizes the need for adaptations to control internal temperature. The **terrestrial environment** is one in which water is generally in short supply. Terrestrial organisms have had to evolve structures and physiological mechanisms to obtain and conserve water. Air, the gas supporting most of the body of a terrestrial animal, is very low in density. Therefore, terrestrial animals had to evolve stronger support structures and different mechanism of locomotion. Organisms that spend most of their time in an aerial environment and have evolved the ability to fly have had to specialize in other ways. Adaptations to flight include low density and wings (airfoils) whose structure provides a large surface area for lift and mechanisms for maneuvering in the air. It is very informative to study aquatic animals such as whales that have evolved from terrestrial animals. Through convergent evolution these formerly terrestrial organisms have developed structural and functional characteristics that are similar to the adaptations seen in primitively aquatic organisms.

CLASS CHONDRICHTHYES: THE SHARKS AND THEIR RELATIVES

Examine the preserved shark and skeleton and the diagram. The skeleton is composed of cartilage. These fish have a well-developed cranium and vertebral column. Note the paired anterior and posterior fins. Study the pictures of the musculature; note that it is definitely segmented. You will see this in the bony fish as well. How does segmented axial musculature function to create locomotion? The sharks have well-developed jaws, which have evolved from the supports of most anterior gill slits. These animals belong to the Gnathostomata group. Study this word. What is the meaning of the prefix and suffix?

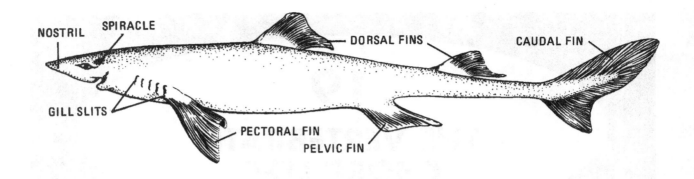

NOSTRIL SPIRACLE DORSAL FINS CAUDAL FIN
GILL SLITS PECTORAL FIN PELVIC FIN

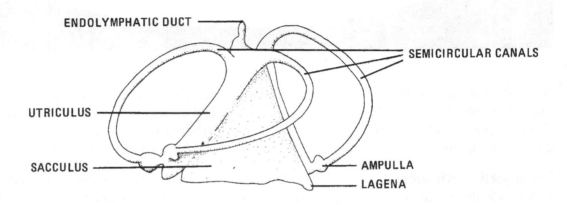

ENDOLYMPHATIC DUCT SEMICIRCULAR CANALS
UTRICULUS
SACCULUS AMPULLA LAGENA

LEFT EAR OF THE DOGFISH SHARK

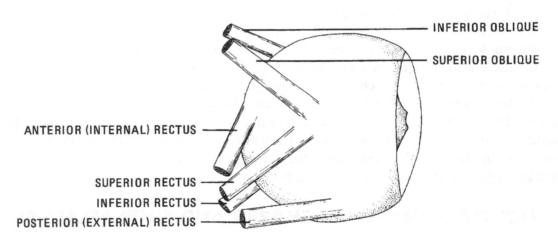

INFERIOR OBLIQUE
SUPERIOR OBLIQUE
ANTERIOR (INTERNAL) RECTUS
SUPERIOR RECTUS
INFERIOR RECTUS
POSTERIOR (EXTERNAL) RECTUS

RIGHT EYE OF DOGFISH SHARK, DORSAL VIEW, SHOWING ATTACHMENT OF MUSCLES

DOGFISH SHARK, EXTERNAL APPEARANCE
AND DETAILS OF STRUCTURE, EYE AND EAR

A Typical Shark

CLASS OSTEICHTHYES: THE BONY FISH

Study the preserved specimens and the diagrams of representative Actinopterygii (ray-finned) bony fish. Observe the preserved skeleton. Note that the bones are delicate. Compare them to the bones of terrestrial animals of the same size. Note that these fish have paired anterior (pectoral) and posterior (pelvic) fins, although in many advanced Osteichthyes the pelvic fins have often migrated far to the anterior. Study the diagram of the muscles. Why are they so obviously segmented? What is the primary function of fins in the Osteichthyes and the Chondricthyes? Study the diagram and the preserved specimen of the fish and find the swim bladder. In the bony fish this organ functions as a buoyancy regulating structure.

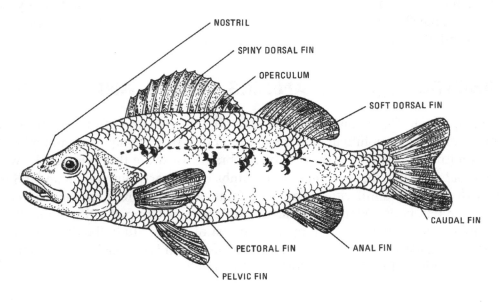

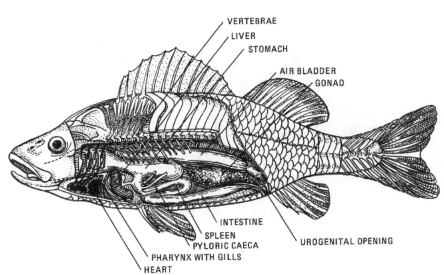

PERCH, EXTERNAL APPEARANCE AND LATERAL DISSECTION

A Typical Bony Fish

Study the picture of the Coelacanth. This fish belongs to the Sarcopterygean (fleshy-finned) group of the Osteichthyes. Note the large, fleshy, paired anterior and pelvic fins. Look at the diagram of the bone structure in these fish. Most of the members of this group of fishes are extinct. Many have the swim bladder attached to the pharynx and are able to use it as an auxiliary gas exchange organ by swimming to the surface of the water and gulping air. What adaptive advantage would this provide the fish?

Study the living fish in the tank. Describe the mechanism of swimming. You may need to watch for some period of time to observe fast swimming. Which fin is used in producing rapid swimming motion? Determine the role of all of the fins on a fish. Examine the skeleton of a fish and a picture of the muscle arrangement. How does the swimming process relate to body structure (skeletal and muscular)? Compare the fish skeleton to the skeletons of the terrestrial vertebrates. How are they similar? How and why are they different?

CLASS AMPHIBIA: SALAMANDERS, TOADS, AND FROGS

Examine the amphibian display and diagrams. Examine the skeleton of the Necturus, an example of a typical terrestrial amphibian, and the skeleton of a frog, an aquatic amphibian. Compare the fish skeleton to the skeletons of these two vertebrates. How are they similar? How and why are they different? Examine the drawings of the limbs of the early amphibian and a Sarcopterygean fish. Note the similarities. The paired fins of the fish are homologous to the paired appendages of the tetrapods. What is the meaning of the term tetrapod? Study the diagrams of the musculature of the Necturus and compare it to that of a fish. Study the diagrams of the locomotion in the salamanders. How much are the limbs used and how much is the whole body bent? How is this reflected in the musculoskeletal system?

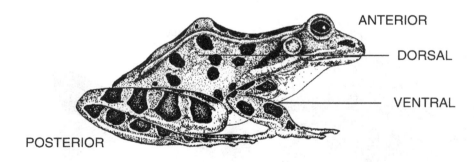

LATERAL VIEW OF LEOPARD FROG

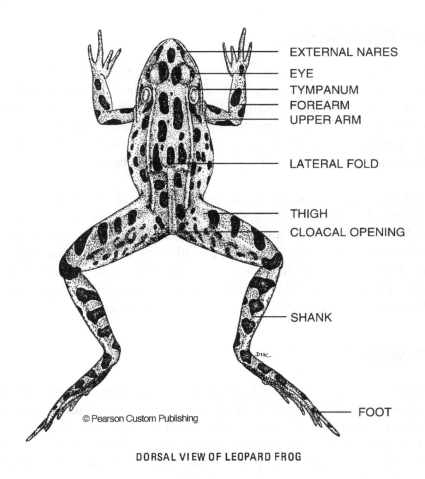

EXTERNAL NARES
EYE
TYMPANUM
FOREARM
UPPER ARM

LATERAL FOLD

THIGH
CLOACAL OPENING

SHANK

FOOT

© Pearson Custom Publishing

DORSAL VIEW OF LEOPARD FROG

Study the living frog in the display tank. It and other frogs swim using the powerful legs and webbed feet.

SUBPHYLUM: AMNIOTA

CLASS: REPTILIA

Examine the reptile display. Study the skeletons and diagrams of skeletons of selected reptiles. Compare the reptile skeleton to the skeletons with those of amphibians. How are they similar? How and why are they different? Compare the diagrams of the musculature of the amphibian and a lizard. Note the reduced segmentation and the relative increase in the musculature limbs. What are the major adaptations of reptiles that allow them to live in dry environments? Observe that the reptiles are very diverse and that some have evolved adaptations for living in the aquatic environment. Compare the diagrams of the skeletal systems of these aquatic reptiles with those of fish. Note the similarities and differences. This is an excellent example of convergent evolution.

Examine the living reptiles. Note the very great difference between the lizard and the snake. Both are terrestrial, but have evolved very different adaptations for locomotion. Can you think of some benefits for the legless adaptation of the snakes?

CLASS AVES: THE BIRDS

In both anatomy and physiology the birds are very similar to the reptiles. In fact, the Aves have evolved from one of the more advanced groups of the Reptilia. Birds are adapted to powered flight, as opposed to gliding. Powered flight requires highly adapted wings (airfoils), strong muscles, and lightweight bodies (low density). Observe the skeleton of the bird. Note the many fused parts of the skeleton. This provides strength and reduces weight. Study the pictures of bird bones. Note that they are thin-walled and hollow, which reduces weight.

The diagram of the flight muscles shows an adaptation for increased muscle power. Whereas flying reptiles and mammals have the wing lowering muscles ventral and the wing elevating muscles dorsal, in birds both sets of muscles are ventral. The sternum is keeled to provide a large area for attachment of these muscles. The wing elevating muscle, supracoracoideus, is attached to the dorsal side of the wing by a tendon that passes though a hole formed at the union of the wing support bones. Find this hole (the supracoracoideus foramen) and figure out the mechanics of the system. Which part of the chicken has the most meat? Why?

CLASS MAMMALIA

Examine the mammal display. Study the skeleton of a typical mammal, the cat. Examine the model skeleton of an atypical mammal, the human. What skeletal changes have accompanied the evolution of bipedal locomotion? (Clue, look at the hind legs and support bones and the spinal column). Compare the mammal skeletons with the skeletons of the other groups you have studied. How are they similar? How and why are they different? Study the drawings of the musculature of the cat. Compare them with the muscles of other groups you have studied. Look at the diagrams comparing aquatic mammals with aquatic fishes and reptiles. This is an example of convergent evolution. Does it matter if the tail fin is vertical or horizontal? How does the swimming movement of a fish with a vertical tail fin differ from that of a whale with a horizontal tail fin? Look at the pictures that show the diversity of mammals.

MAMMAL DISSECTION: THE RAT

The objective of this exercise is multi-leveled: (1) To provide you with some understanding of the internal structure of a complex organism. (2) To introduce you to the art of dissection and the use of dissection tools. (3) To provide you with a basic knowledge of the anatomy of a rat for use in advanced laboratory courses such as Comparative Anatomy and Physiology.

Most of the dissection will be performed using the scissors for cutting and a probe and forceps for locating and moving organs. The scalpel may be used occasionally to cut; however the flat, non-blade end is useful in separating organs and tissues. Before getting your rat, protect your hands with surgical gloves that are provided at the front table. Read the following dissection instructions carefully and identify the organs. You may see a dissected rat on the laboratory examination.

EXTERNAL EXAMINATION

If the animal smells strongly of preservative, rinse it in the sink and remove the excess water with a paper towel. Observe the head and note the eyes, the nose (rhinarium) the ears (pinna), the mouth which leads into the oral cavity, and the whiskers (vibrissae). Most of the body is covered by hair of varying length and degrees of coarseness. What is the primary function of hair in mammals? Observe the external genitalia to determine if you have a male or female. Make sure that you study a specimen of both sexes.

INTERNAL EXAMINATION

Place the animal ventral side up in the dissection pan. Using the forceps to lift the skin on the mid-ventral line. Make a small cut adjacent to the forceps with the scissors. Insert the scissors into the hole you just produced and cut in the anterior direction to the chin and in the posterior direction to the anus, cutting around both sides of the external genitalia. Make a cut from the midventral cut out to the legs. Using the handle of the scalpel, separate the skin from the under-lying muscle. Note that the muscles are covered with a layer of connective tissue, the fascia.

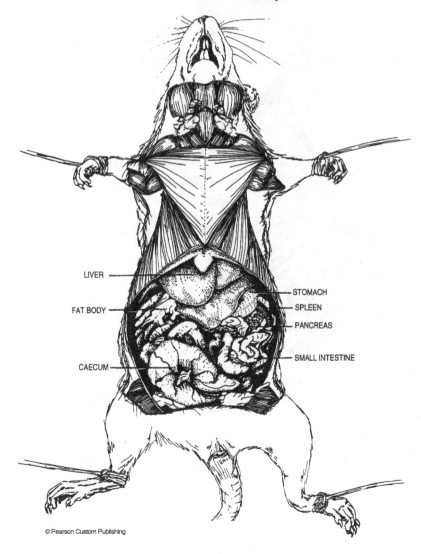

LIVER

FAT BODY

CAECUM

STOMACH

SPLEEN

PANCREAS

SMALL INTESTINE

© Pearson Custom Publishing

RAT, DISSECTION OF ABDOMINAL CAVITY

Open the wall of the abdominal cavity by lifting the midventral muscles with forceps and cutting as you did to cut the skin. When you have finished, the dissection should appear like the drawing above. Using this figure identify the stomach, spleen, liver, pancreas, small intestine, cacum, and fat body. Move the cacum aside and observe more pancreatic tissue, the esophagus leading into the stomach, the pyloric sphincter, spleen, duodenum, small intestine (jejunum and ileum), colon, and rectum. When you have finished, the dissection should look like the drawing below.

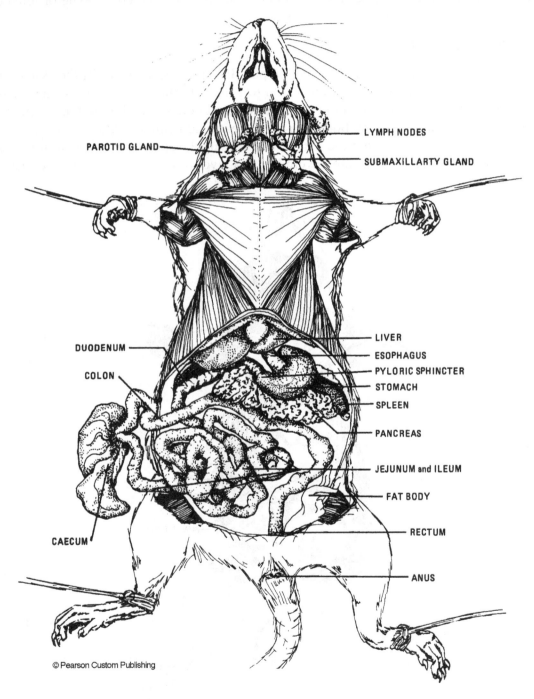

PAROTID GLAND

LYMPH NODES

SUBMAXILLARTY GLAND

DUODENUM

COLON

LIVER

ESOPHAGUS

PYLORIC SPHINCTER

STOMACH

SPLEEN

PANCREAS

JEJUNUM and ILEUM

FAT BODY

RECTUM

CAECUM

ANUS

RAT, DIGESTIVE TRACT DISSECTION

Open the wall of the thoracic cavity by cutting with the scissors along the left and right sides of the rib cage. Grasp the posterior edge of the sternum and lift it. Cut the muscular diaphragm away from the ribs to expose the lungs and the heart. Cut in the anterior direction on both sides of the neck to expose the trachea and its two major branches, the bronchi. Find the esophagus that joins the oral cavity to the stomach. You may also see the right and left common carotid arteries, the parotid salivary glands, and some lymph nodes. Return to the thoracic cavity and observe that each lung is divided into lobes. The heart is within a thin-walled pericardial sac. Open this sac and observe the ventricles and atria of the heart. You may also see the major veins returning the blood to the heart. The left and right precava return blood from the head and neck, and the postcava returns blood from the rest of the body.

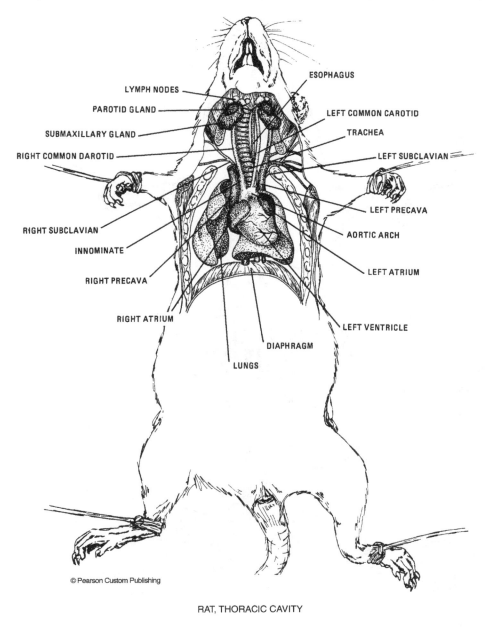

LYMPH NODES
PAROTID GLAND
SUBMAXILLARY GLAND
RIGHT COMMON DAROTID
RIGHT SUBCLAVIAN
INNOMINATE
RIGHT PRECAVA
RIGHT ATRIUM
LUNGS
DIAPHRAGM

ESOPHAGUS
LEFT COMMON CAROTID
TRACHEA
LEFT SUBCLAVIAN
LEFT PRECAVA
AORTIC ARCH
LEFT ATRIUM
LEFT VENTRICLE

© Pearson Custom Publishing

RAT, THORACIC CAVITY

Thoracic Cavity

Return to the abdominal cavity. Note that the liver is divided into lobes. Carefully cut the liver out of the cavity using scissors. With the forceps lift the intestine and note that it is suspended by a thin mesentery. The mesentery may contain considerable fat, especially in older male rats. Carefully remove the stomach, intestines, spleen, and pancreas to expose the urogenital system. The large bean-shaped organs are the kidneys. Note the large arteries and veins that carry blood to and from the kidney. Each kidney drains into a duct, the ureter, which leads to the urinary bladder. At this point your dissection should look like the figures. If you have a male observe the testes, which are located in the scrotum. Leading from each testis is a vas deferens, which passes through the prostate gland and into the penis. If your rat is a female find the ovaries and the two horns of the uterus. The uterus may be rather difficult to find if the animal is young. Look at the rat from another group to see the genital system of the opposite sex from your rat.

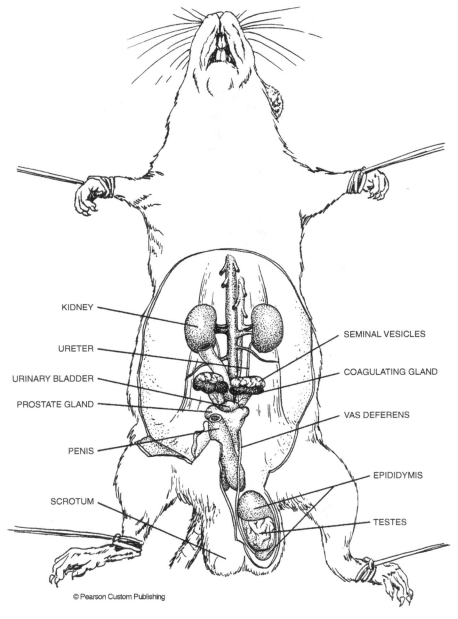

RAT, MALE UROGENITAL SYSTEM

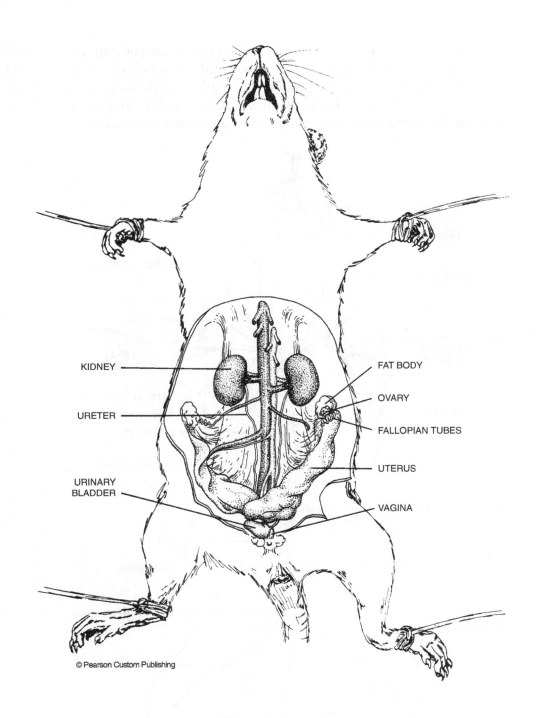

KIDNEY

URETER

URINARY
BLADDER

FAT BODY

OVARY

FALLOPIAN TUBES

UTERUS

VAGINA

© Pearson Custom Publishing

RAT, FEMALE UROGENITAL SYSTEM

Using the drawings below, identify as many of the labeled vessels as you can. You should be able to see the following arteries: the paired common carotid and subclavian arteries, which are anterior. Find the single thoracic-abdominal artery, which gives off the paired renal arteries and common iliac arteries. The veins have thinner walls and are more difficult to find. Look for the right and left precava, the single post cava, and the paired common iliac veins.

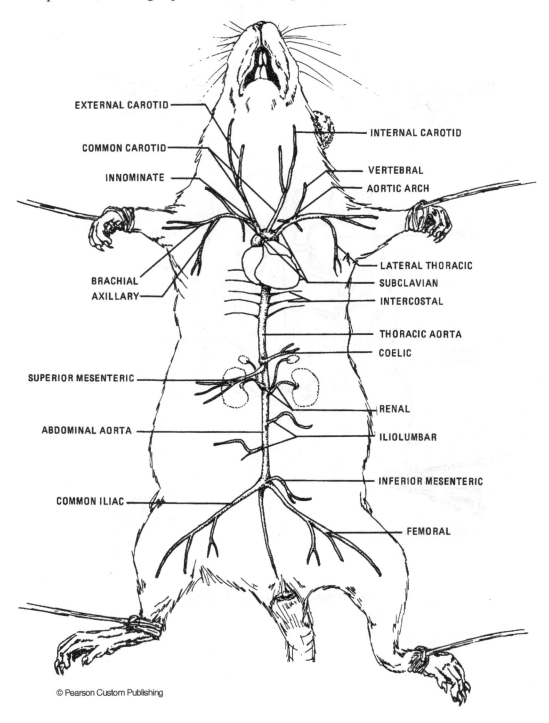

RAT ARTERIES

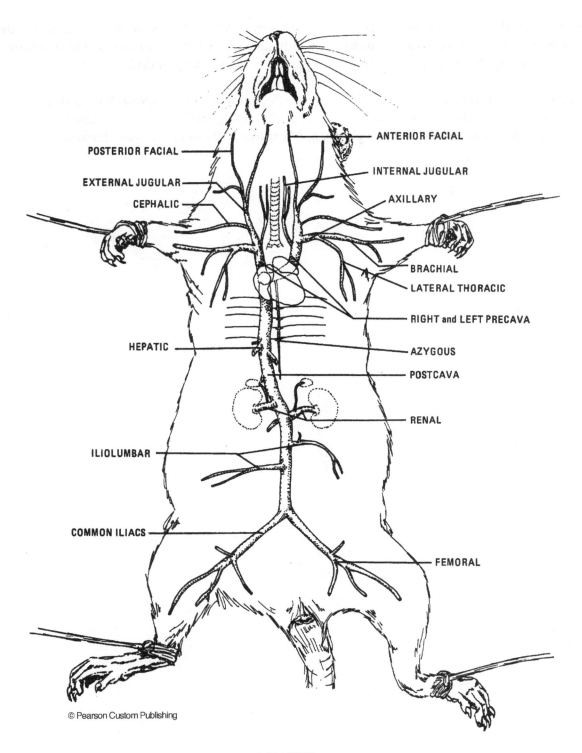

POSTERIOR FACIAL

EXTERNAL JUGULAR

CEPHALIC

ANTERIOR FACIAL

INTERNAL JUGULAR

AXILLARY

BRACHIAL

LATERAL THORACIC

RIGHT and LEFT PRECAVA

AZYGOUS

POSTCAVA

RENAL

HEPATIC

ILIOLUMBAR

COMMON ILIACS

FEMORAL

© Pearson Custom Publishing

RAT VEINS

We will not dissect and identify the muscles. However, you may find it interesting to remove the skin from a hind leg and attempt to find the individual muscles. To do this you must remove the fascia covering the muscles to reveal the separations between the individual muscles.

When you have finished the dissection put the specimen into the disposal bag as directed by your laboratory instructor. Carefully clean your dissecting tools and return them to the proper location. Remove your gloves and dispose of them in the wastebasket.

CHAPTER 19 REVIEW QUESTIONS (2 POINTS EACH)

Name_____

1.   What are two locomotion types among the Reptiles?

2.   What are two ways organisms have evolved to adapt to aerial locomotion?

3.   List two specimens of the class *Reptilia* that were set out in lab today.

4.   What are two functions of fins on fish?

5.   Name the fins on the bony fish.